# MAKING SMALL
# WORKSHOP TOOLS

# MAKING SMALL
# WORKSHOP TOOLS

**Stan Bray**

**NEXUS SPECIAL INTERESTS**

Nexus Special Interests Ltd
Nexus House
Boundary Way
Hemel Hempstead
Hertfordshire HP2 7ST
England

First published 1987
Reprinted 1991, 1994, 1997

ISBN 0 85242 886 3

Phototypesetting by Photocomp Ltd, Birmingham

Printed and bound in Great Britain by
Biddles Ltd, Guildford and King's Lynn

# Contents

# Introduction

Making tools and workshop equipment forms the major part of the model engineering hobby for some, but for others it is regarded as something of a chore, the manufacture of models being the prime concern. Frequently, however, there is a need for items that cannot always be purchased, or perhaps are needed at a time when obtaining them is not convenient. In these instances making the necessary tools or whatever becomes the only possible solution.

The reasons for a reluctance to undertake making these items are that there is a common belief that their manufacture will be very time-consuming, or that special materials will be needed. Neither is true – all the tools described in this book can be made in a very short time, some in fact in a matter of minutes and none requires anything other than the type of material likely to be found in any home workshop, left over from other projects. They are designed to use up those little short ends that get put away just in case they will come in useful, but never do! I prefer to convert them into useful things for my workshop rather than just leave odd bits of metal in a box under the bench to go rusty.

The projects are divided into sections for convenience. They are designed generally for marking out, benchwork or lathe work, but there are also some fixtures suitable for use on any type of machinery. While reasonable care is required in their manufacture they do not need either high precision or, unless it is the constructor's wish, a high finish. The important thing is that they work and that when they have been made they add to the workshop equipment. Personally I have found all of them pleasing little exercises which offer relaxation from more demanding tasks, and they have served me well over the years.

The projects are suitable for the beginner, but at the same time the more advanced worker will find them of value and well worth while. Use them to get rid of those odd pieces of material and to while away the odd hour or so when it is not always possible to proceed with the longer tasks. While I have made this sort of thing for years, having been encouraged to do so when employed in engineering, they started their life in print under the heading "Bray's Bench" in *Model Engineer*, and from correspondence I have received they have without doubt proved to be highly popular projects. It is difficult to imagine my workshop without most of them, as they are used so frequently, and many I have made in several versions, as the metal has come to hand, since they are the sort of things that have more often than not proved useful for a variety of purposes.

I am quite certain that readers who make them will be delighted with the added versatility they give to the workshop as well as finding that work can be carried out far more quickly than before.

# A Scriber

A scriber is a simple tool used for marking lines on metal. It is drawn along the metal and this causes a scratch which can be seen and therefore used as a guide for working. If marking fluid is applied to the metal first then the scratch becomes even more pronounced and easier to see. In order that it retains its point the metal used for making the scriber should be hardened and tempered: we temper metal because if it is left hard it becomes too brittle and liable to break.

All then that we really need to make a scriber is a piece of steel which is pointed and which we can harden and temper, and the usual material is silver steel. This of course will work quite satisfactorily but it does have disadvantages. Firstly, smooth steel tends to slide about in one's hands, making gripping rather a problem and if we cannot grip the scriber firmly we cannot draw our lines accurately. Also the size of steel required to obtain the necessary point is not very large, and this too makes such a scriber difficult to hold. The third reason may only apply to me, but I find that small tools disappear in my workshop. For many years now I have been quite convinced that a little

man lives under my bench and survives on drills, taps, scribers, etc. He seems to get well satisfied, and in fact when I uprooted and moved house and workshop thinking I had at last rid myself of his presence he must have slipped on the removal van, as he is still at it. I therefore have found that a fairly large non-slip scriber is the answer to such problems. Not only is it too heavy for my unwanted friend to lift but the bulk makes scribing lines very easy. Far easier, in fact, in my opinion, than a scriber bought in a toolshop, as I do not think that the commercially made ones have the required bulk.

Manufacture of the tool is very simple, and I suggest a piece of ⅜in. or 10mm diameter mild steel for the body. Mild steel is not essential and in fact brass or alloy would do as well, but steel is cheaper. The first thing to do is to turn down one end to a diameter of ⁵⁄₁₆in. or 7mm for a length of ¾in. or 20mm and face across the end. Without taking the steel from the chuck, centre drill and drill the end; I suggest either ⅛in. or 3mm for the hole which is to take the scriber point. You can go as large as ³⁄₁₆in. or 5mm if you wish, as long as the diameter is the same as the steel used for the point. The length of the hole should be about 1in. or 25mm. Turn the piece of steel round and replace in the chuck. Then remove about the same amount of metal from the other end. Size here is not too important as it is just for appearance. The end then needs to be rounded off, this partly for appearance and partly for comfort. Use a small form tool for doing this.

The metal needs to be turned round again and gripped by the reduced diameter just made, while supported at the other end with a centre in the tailstock. Use the hard centre and do not forget to lubricate it. With the metal supported in this way knurl the length of steel that remains full diameter. When this is finished you need to cross drill and tap the end with the hole in. This is for the retaining screw and I would suggest 6BA or 3mm as suitable sizes for the thread.

The point is a piece of silver steel gently tapered almost to a point and then at the very end a slightly sharper angle of about sixty degrees should be put on. The best way to do this is to make a steady that will support the silver steel while it is being turned. Get a short length of brass or mild steel rod about ¼in. or 6mm diameter. Drill a hole in it the same size as the silver steel being used for the point. Then cut it lengthways along half its diameter and remove the section. Put the remainder in the tailstock chuck and the silver steel can be supported by it while it is turned to a point. The final sixty degrees can be put on with a grindstone after it is hardened. Get as good a finish as you can on the piece as it will get discoloured during hardening and if it is rough it will be difficult to get the discolouring off.

To harden the scriber section, first dip the steel in some washing-up liquid.

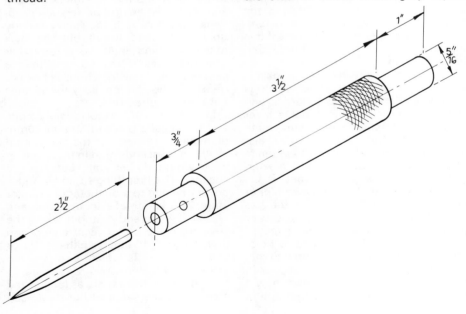

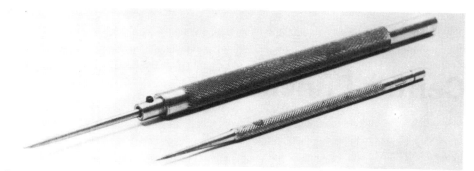

*Comparison of the large scriber detailed with a commercial product.*

Then heat up the non-pointed part until the whole thing goes the colour of a boiled carrot. The colour will actually run into the pointed part. Immediately quench it in cold water. With a little bit of luck the washing-up liquid will have prevented too much discoloration, but anyway the shiny silver colour will have to be brought back by the use of emery paper. When it is thoroughly clean put some fine sand (possibly rob the budgie) in a tin and put the tin on some sort of support. Heat the sand until the scriber section just starts to change colour. It will start to go the faintest brown tinge. Immediately quench in cold water. The temper should be hard enough to mark most metals without being too brittle, just having had the brittleness drawn from it. Had we wanted a slightly softer result we could have let the colour get deeper or even go blue for something like a screwdriver.

All that remains is to put the pointed part in the handle and screw up the locking screw. The scriber is ready for use. When using it remember that it is used with one firm stroke. Lines should never be made with two or three consecutive strokes as this leads to lack of accuracy.

# Centre Punches

There are two types of centre punch. One is really called a dot punch and is used for preliminary marking of a hole position, the other is the true centre punch and is designed to take the drill point as easily as possible. There is not a great deal of difference in the two except that the dot punch has the point at sixty degrees, which enables it to slip into scribed lines easier than the centre punch with its point at ninety degrees. We do not often find very large dot punches as we sometimes do centre punches.

Both are very easy to make from either silver steel or other high carbon steel. If the material used is round, to allow a grip, either turn a series of grooves along the handle or knurl it. One good way of making such punches it to use hexagonal material, in which case there is no need to knurl or anything else as the material shape provides the grip.

Simply chuck the material and turn the two tapers as shown on the drawing. The material can be whatever diameter suits you best. Harden and temper in the usual way by heating until the steel is the colour of a boiled carrot, quenching and then heating in a sand bath after cleaning up until a light straw colour appears and again quenching.

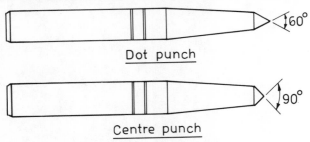

Dot punch

Centre punch

Either turn series of grooves or knurl if using round material.

# Odd-leg Calipers

Odd-leg calipers are used to draw lines parallel to an edge. Frequently known as Odd-Leg Jennies or just plain jennies they consist of one caliper arm and an arm with an adjustable scriber point. The caliper arm has a small step at the end and this is located on the edge of the metal to be marked. The point is adjusted so that it will scribe a mark at the distance from the edge that is required. The calipers are then drawn along the edge of the metal and the resulting scriber mark runs parallel to that edge.

They are a very easy little tool to make and ideally the workshop should contain two or more. This means that when marking out work the calipers can be set as required and another pair set if another measurement is needed, thus saving a considerable amount of work and the possibility of inaccuracies creeping in. They can be set from the end of a metal rule, with the arm at the edge and the point on the required mark.

Start by marking out the arms. You will need two pieces of 1/16in. or 2mm thick mild steel 3/4in. or 20mm wide. One

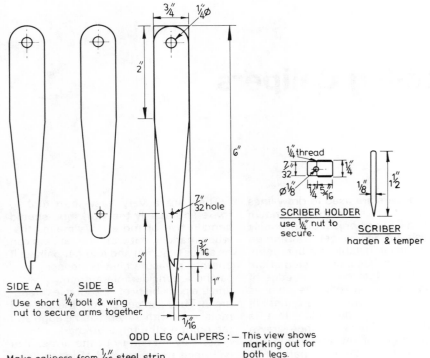

**SIDE A**     **SIDE B**

Use short ¼″ bolt & wing nut to secure arms together.

SCRIBER HOLDER
use ¼″ nut to secure.

SCRIBER
harden & temper

ODD LEG CALIPERS :— This view shows marking out for both legs.

Make calipers from ¹⁄₁₆″ steel strip.
Side A is on top of side B as shown.

should be 6 in. or 150mm long, the other 4½in. or 115mm. Mark both out with the hole positions shown as though both will have two holes drilled in them. Centre punch the places where the holes would be and drill both arms with small holes at the top, but only the shorter arm with one lower down. The hole size is not important as the correct size will be drilled later. The reason for marking the hole position on the long arm is for it to act as a guide when doing the rest of the marking out. Having the dot in that position allows one to see if the angled lines have been marked correctly or not: it is very easy

to get angled lines wrong without some sort of a guide. The longer arm now needs to be marked out using the point shown at the bottom as a further guide to accuracy. Trying to mark the little step in direct, without putting the bottom point in, will almost certainly mean getting it off centre.

When both arms have been marked out to your satisfaction open out the three holes to the finished sizes and then saw and file the arms to shape. Round off the edges when the shape is right, as sharp edges are uncomfortable to work with. The two arms can be held at the top either with a commercial

12

wing nut and short bolt or you can make a large-headed screw with a round-headed nut if you wish. Although imperial sizes have been given on the drawing 6mm will do for the top and 5mm for the lower one will do just as well.

The scriber holder is made from mild steel and is simply a short length turned to a small step and threaded. A hole is put through the middle at the exact edge of the step. It is better to drill the cross hole first and turn the component down afterwards, as getting a hole through at the exact edge of the step would be nigh on impossible. It is, however, most important that the hole is drilled at that point as this lines the scriber point up with the other leg. Again the measurements given are imperial but can easily be converted to metric – 6mm for the larger part, a 5mm thread and a 3mm hole will work nicely. The scriber is a short length of silver steel ⅛in. or 3mm diameter turned to a point and hardened and tempered to a light straw colour. The scriber is held in position either with a commercial nut or you can make a small knurled one specially if you wish.

That is all that there is to it. If you want a pair of dividers simply make two of the legs with scribers and there you are.

# Ruler Holder

I feel a little bit of a cheat describing this gadget in a book on making small tools as it is so basic that it hardly needs making. It is, however, a most useful thing to have, particularly when using the scribing block for marking-out. It enables a ruler to be stood on end and to remain there while measurements are taken from it. The drawing gives measurements but these need not be adhered to. Any piece of rectangular metal bar will do. Slip it in the four-jaw chuck and face off the ends to get it square. Drill and tap a hole for the little plate that will hold the ruler in position and make the recess as shown. This can either be done by putting the block in the lathe toolpost and running a milling cutter along it or simply by putting a slight cut along with a hacksaw and filing the recess in. It will only need to be ⅟₃₂in. or 1mm deep and so filing it accurately is no problem.

Again, the clamping piece need not be the sizes shown as any small piece of metal will do. All it needs is a clearance hole for the screw, and the size of that can be your choice too. The securing screw can be an ordinary slotted screw, or a little knurled-head one can be made. No great pressure will be needed to secure the ruler, which will more or less stand up on its own against the block.

Simple the tool may be, but you will certainly wonder how you ever did without it once you have made it.

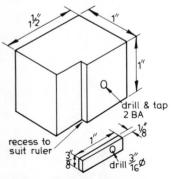

RULER HOLDER FOR MARKING OUT
Ruler set in recess head with clamp and slotted screw.

14

# A Small Scribing Block

A scribing block, or surface gauge as it may be called, has many uses in model engineering. It is a means of setting a scriber to a set height and retaining that height while it is used for a particular purpose. For example, if we wish to scribe a line on a piece of sheet metal we can measure with a rule the point where the line is to be scribed, make a mark at one end and a mark at the other, hold the rule on both those marks and then scribe along it. We *should* have our line accurately along the metal where we want it, but will we? It is most unlikely. When we put the scriber to the rule there is bound to be a slight angular movement, not very great but it is there. The chances of getting that angle exactly the same at each end is pretty slim. There must be a slight angle when we draw the scriber along. Again it is doubtful if we can retain it exactly

*Two slightly different sizes of the tool, also showing different angles of the scriber.*

the whole length of the line, so although it is quite minute there is a variation in the distance the scriber point is from the rule.

Our scribing block will prevent this from happening. True, the accuracy will still depend on the operator, but at least there is slightly less possibility of a mishap occurring. We will need a flat surface, though, and for that we will need a surface plate, which is a hefty chunk of ground cast iron which has been tested for flatness, or, if you have a flat lathe bed then you can wind the saddle out of the way and use that, or you can pay a visit to a high quality glass merchant and get a piece of thick plate glass. The sort of glass used for shop windows is what is needed, and it is perfectly flat as the method of manufacture makes it so.

The scribing block can also be used for measuring the height of your lathe tools to ensure they are correct and for getting precise measurements from components. To do this we lay the component on our surface plate, put the scribing block next to it with the point touching the place where we wish to measure, and then tighten it well up. Set a pair of inside calipers from the surface plate to touch the point on the scribing block and then use a micrometer or vernier gauge to measure the distance between the prongs on the inside calipers.

The tool being described is much easier to make than the type of scribing

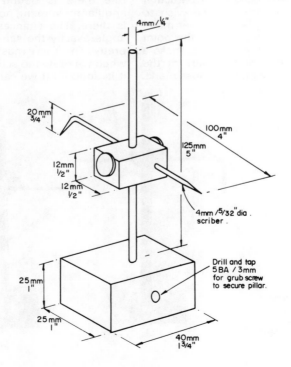

4mm / ¼"

20 mm
¾"

12mm
½"

12 mm
½"

100mm
4"

125mm
5"

4mm /⁵⁄₃₂" dia.
scriber.

Drill and tap
5 BA / 3mm
for grub screw
to secure pillar.

25 mm
1"

25 mm
1"

40mm
1¾"

*Machining the square base for the scriber block.*

block sold commercially. The choice of movement on it is much more limited, but it will do the job just as well and because of its simplicity leaves less possibility of error during manufacture. Unlike many of the items described in this book it is possible to give measurements for the components. Even so there is plenty of room to manoeuvre and other sizes of material can be used if these happen to be easily available.

## THE BASE

This is made from a piece of 1in. or 25mm square mild steel bar 1¾in. or 40mm long. It is first of all held in the four-jaw chuck and both the ends where it has been cut faced to get a nice even surface, then it should be removed and the burrs filed off. If you cannot get hold of a suitable piece of material of this type then a 1in. or 25mm length of round bar will do, the diameter to be 1½in. or 35mm. The use of round stock has a slight disadvantage as the square base can sometimes be used as a guide along the work, which is not so easy with a round one.

A hole needs to be drilled centrally in the base and it must be at exactly ninety degrees. For this reason the use of a drilling machine is not recommended and the work should be carried out in the lathe. The circular type base will be quite straightforward – just put the metal, which has of course been faced both sides, in the three-jaw chuck, centre drill and then drill the exact diameter for the centre pillar. In the case of the square base the point for drilling will need to be centre punched and then the work mounted in the four-jaw chuck so that the centre punch mark is near enough on the centre of rotation of the lathe. I say near enough because this is one time when a slight lack of accuracy will not be too disastrous and as long as the hole is at ninety degrees, if it is a fraction nearer one edge than another will not make any difference to the operation of the tool.

The centre pillar will require holding in the hole and for this I suggest either that you use a retaining compound of good strength or you cross drill and tap a hole to take a small grub screw which tightens up on to the pillar. One advantage of the latter method is that it is

17

*Drilling the square base in the four-jaw chuck.*

possible to put in different length pillars should the need arise. This cannot be done with retaining compound.

## THE CENTRE PILLAR

The easiest job you will ever have. Just a piece of mild or silver steel between ³/₁₆in. or 4mm and ¼in. or 6mm diameter, or maybe even a fraction thicker if you like. Face each end and that is all you need. I put a little knob on the top of mine in an idle moment but that was just personal choice and made absolutely no difference whatever to the function of the tool.

## THE SMALL BLOCK

This is from mild steel and you will see that it has four holes in it. Start as usual by facing the ends, then preferably put the holes in with the block in the lathe. If, however, you find it more convenient they can be done on the drilling machine. Two of the holes will need to be tapped.

## THE SCRIBER

This is made of silver steel and the first job is to put the point on each end. This should really be turned on using a very

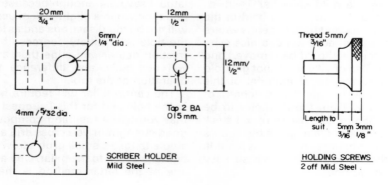

20 mm
¾"

6mm/
¼"dia.

4mm/⁵/₃₂"dia.

SCRIBER HOLDER
Mild Steel .

12mm
½"

12mm/
½"

Tap 2 BA
0 15 mm.

Thread 5mm/
³/₁₆"

Length to
suit.   5mm 3mm
³/₁₆" ⅛"

HOLDING SCREWS
2 off Mild Steel .

18

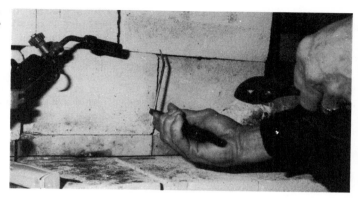

*Heating the scriber to bend one point to the desired angle.*

sharp cutting tool. In practice what will happen to many readers is that the metal when it gets to its thinnest point will start to move away from the tool and eventually possibly even climb on top of it. To prevent this drill a couple of holes in a piece of old angle iron and screw a wooden block to it. (Actually chipboard works well.) Bolt the angle to the cross slide so the wood is touching the work then you can turn the point with no trouble. The silver steel will wear a slight groove in the wood as it is turned and this is to your advantage. After each cut just tap the wood in a little so that it remains in contact with the silver steel and in this way it is possible not only to turn on the point but to get a really good finish as well. Many people resort to filing these sort of jobs. If the work is supported by a piece of wooden dowel in the tailstock this will work. It is a very dangerous practice though, with a good chance of knuckles being rapped on the revolving chuck or clothing catching in it. Far better to be safe.

When the points have been turned on each end the scriber will need to be bent to whatever angle you wish for one end. Heat it until it is the colour of a boiled carrot and holding it close to where it is to be bent with a pair of pliers, use another pair to bend it over. Clean it up when cool until it is bright, and then dip one end in some liquid soap. Heat it to the boiled carrot colour again and quickly, before it can lose any heat, quench it in cold water. This will harden it. However, it will harden it a little too much and so the temper will have to be drawn. It will need to be cleaned to a bright colour again, and this is where dipping it in the soap should have helped, as it makes it easier to clean up.

It is now a case of heating each end until it turns a light straw colour and then quenching again. Do not heat the tip directly but heat it a little way from it and allow the colour to run. So we will get the effect of the place where the heat is applied being a dark brown or even a light blue and the tip a light straw, it must be quenched at once. For small components that are being tempered I use a sand bath. This is not really practical in this case but the scriber could be tempered by laying it on a piece of steel plate, and heating the plate from underneath until the scriber colour changes. The advantage to this

19

method is that there is more control over the colour than when the scriber is heated direct.

## ADJUSTING SCREWS

There are two screws needed, one to adjust the scriber length in the block and the other to adjust the height of the block on the pillar. A drawing is given of a suitable knob but an ordinary commercial screw could be used if one so desired. Another idea is to use a length of threaded rod with a commercial wing nut secured to it with retaining compound. These wing nuts I find give a lot of torque when tightening up and I frequently use them. They can be purchased at any good ironmongers or tool stockists and are very cheap to buy.

# Engineer's Bevel

When marking out it is frequently necessary to scribe lines at an angle. It is possible to use a combination set, although on small items this is somewhat unwieldy, or one can purchase an engineer's protractor, a highly efficient instrument which is very expensive. Is it worth the expense for a hobby, one must ask, and the answer must be with the individual. Having in mind the fact that the need for these angled lines will not be all that frequent, there is an alternative, in the form of the bevel. This can be set to any angle required and to do so all that is needed is a cheap protractor of the type used by schoolchildren. Such a tool can be purchased but again it is very easy to make, and while in the description given measurements are supplied, as long as proportions remain the same, bevels can be made to any size to suit a particular job. Making this one involves mainly handwork and it is described with this in view. The use of a milling machine or even a vertical slide for the lathe can make the construction even easier. The one I made purely for the purpose of this chapter was made entirely by hand

*The completed tool – a simple job.*

except for the nut and screw and took only an afternoon to complete from start to finish.

It is difficult to give a name to the various parts and so we will call the first piece to be constructed the upright. It consists of a piece of mild steel ¾in. or 40mm × ⅜in. or 10mm in section, which is a standard strip. The piece will need to be 3½in. or 85mm long after you have

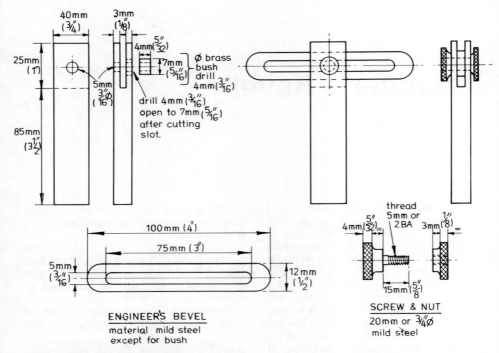

**ENGINEER'S BEVEL**
material mild steel
except for bush

**SCREW & NUT**
20mm or ¾"∅
mild steel

squared the ends, although obviously slightly shorter or longer than this will do no harm. I always square the ends in the lathe using the four-jaw chuck, but they can be filed or milled if so desired. Put marking fluid on one wide and one narrow side and mark off and drill the hole in the wider side, but at this stage do not drill full diameter.

Mark the two lines for the slot on the smaller side and in the middle of this and ¹⁄₁₆in. or 1.5mm above the lower edge of where it will be make a centre punch mark. Drill right through this with a ³⁄₃₂in. or 2mm drill. This should give a hole that just clears the lines scribed for the slot. Very carefully hacksaw down inside these lines until you reach the hole and then with a warding file open

out until the slot is exactly to the marks. Be careful not to set up a rocking motion with the file. To do this will result either going too large on one edge or the slot being narrower in the centre than at the edges. In fact this is a classic case for filing correctly. Get down as low as possible to the work and use a push stroke only. It may seem somewhat time-consuming but it is the only way to get it right. To check the slot use the piece of ⅛in. or 3mm × ½in. or 12mm steel that will be used for the adjustable bar.

When the slot is completed open out the hole on the large flat to the finished size. To prevent bending the metal at the slot use a small piece of mild steel of the correct thickness to fill the slot as a support. Drill through it and then afterwards it can be discarded.

The movable bar needs coating with marking fluid and marking-out for the slot. Also make a central line along the length. At intervals of 5/32in. or 3.5mm make centre punch marks along this central line and drill through with first a 1/8in. or 3mm drill, opening the holes out afterwards to 5/32in. or 3.5mm. If your measuring has been right the holes will just break into each other. If not and one hole starts to run into the next while drilling do not go ahead but leave that particular one as it can be dealt with afterwards. The slot now needs to be sawn and filed out. I use a piercing saw for the initial breakthrough and then needle files and a small warding file to complete the job. You may find that draw filing is the best way to get the slot edges even. In the drawings the slot is shown with round ends. This is optional and some readers will find that because of slight lack of accuracy in either marking-out or drilling it is not possible to leave them round, in which case square the ends off with a file. The outer ends of the bar are also shown rounded. This is to make life easy for the reader. Correctly speaking there should be a forty-five degree angle across one end and a right angle at the other. Getting these angles accurate is very difficult and if they cannot be exact they are better not there at all.

The screw is a fairly easy turning job. Turn and thread the smaller part first. The next largest diameter follows, and here it is shown to have a rounded shoulder. That is for appearance only and so if you do not fancy rounding the shoulder off leave well alone and keep it square. Finally knurl the full diameter and part off. Making the nut smaller is a similar series of operations. Drill and tap first, turn the step and knurl and part off.

One small item remains, a little brass bush to fit the slot in the adjustable bar and to just go into the hole in the upright. It needs therefore to be the same diameter as the slot in the adjustable bar is wide, have a hole in it to clear the thread of the screw, and to be 1/32in. or 1mm longer than the width of the slot in the upright. This will allow the screw to tighten up and close the slot, so that it grips on the adjustable bar, and at the same time it stops the adjustment being sloppy.

To use the tool simply set it to the required angle and then use it as one would a normal engineer's square. It is also possible to check angles on components by the reverse procedure.

# A Centre Square

This is the sort of tool one rarely purchases, and in fact is not often seen in the tool stockists' catalogues anyway, a rather surprising thing when one stops to think of how much time can be saved by using it. For anyone who is not sure what it does then let me point out that it is used for finding the centre of round bars. It is simply laid across the end and a line scribed along it. It is then laid across at or near a right angle and another line scribed; where the lines meet is the centre of the bar. This saves a lot of juggling that is otherwise required.

All that we need is a piece of bright mild steel some 4½in. or 110mm long and 2in. or 50mm wide. After covering one side with the inevitable marking fluid scribe a line along the centre. Put two centre punch marks on this line, one about ¼in. or 6mm from the end and the other 1in. or 25mm further along. Set a pair of dividers to just over half the distance between these two marks and scribe arcs as shown in the drawing. Centre punch where they meet and drill a hole ⅛in. or 3mm at both points. This ensures that the two holes are on a line exactly at right angles to the line scribed along the steel. Trying to do it with a square could result in lack of accuracy if the scribed line has by

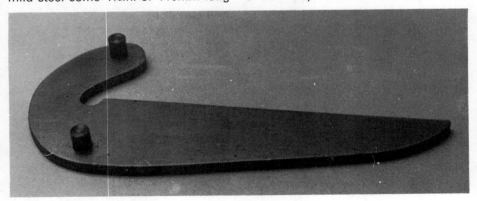

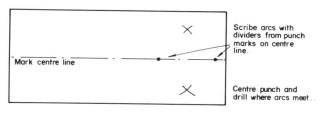

Mark centre line

Scribe arcs with dividers from punch marks on centre line.

Centre punch and drill where arcs meet..

**Method of Marking Out in Order to Ensure Pins are Square to Centre Line**

any chance wandered, and this is quite possible when using odd-leg calipers.

Mark off a spot some ⅛in. or 3mm to one side of the line and the same distance towards the end of the plate from a line drawn between the two holes. The exact position is not important. Centre punch where the mark comes and drill a hole there. The only essential thing is that the hole must go over the edge of the centre line a little. This means that the size of the hole will depend on how accurately you have made the mark. Scribe round the plate to roughly the shape shown on the drawing. I did mine freehand but a set of French Curves could be a useful aid. Carefully cut round the line and file smooth. Then even more carefully cut

along the centre line. Do not go over it as accuracy here is essential. Finish with a file so that the edge is exactly where the line had been. This is important for the tool to work properly.

From a piece of ¹⁄₁₆in. or 4mm mild steel turn two little pegs as shown. If they are to be press-fitted in the holes they need to be just a little larger in diameter than the holes, and a little smaller if using a retainer such as Loctite or Permabond. Apart from putting a nice finish on the plate that is all there is to it. It is possible to tap the two holes and insert cap screws in place of the pegs, but to do so you must make absolutely certain that the tap goes through at a right angle in order to maintain the accuracy.

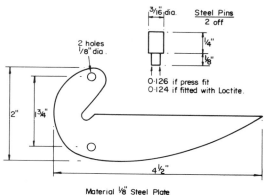

$^{3}/16$ dia.

**Steel Pins**
2 off

¼"

⅛"

0·126 if press fit
0·124 if fitted with Loctite.

2 holes
⅛" dia.

2"

1¾"

4½"

Material ⅛" Steel Plate

# A Trammel

Sometimes a job comes up requiring an arc to be struck or points to be marked out at a distance well beyond the scope of the largest dividers in the workshop. Using a ruler to mark a distance allows errors to creep in and is no use at all for describing a large-radius arc or circle. So how do we do it?

The answer is a trammel. This is a tool fitted, like dividers, with two

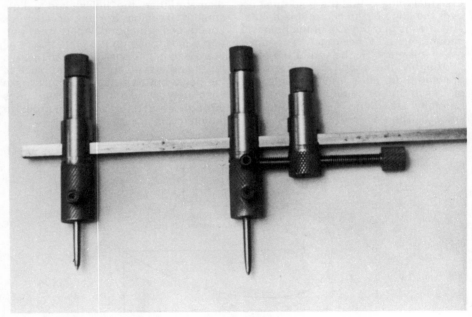

*The completed trammel. All parts have been brought to one end for the photograph.*

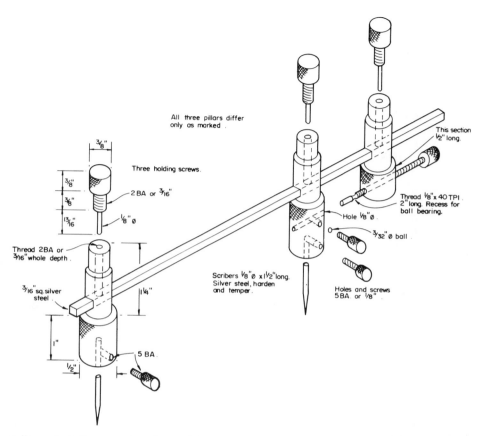

All three pillars differ only as marked.

3/8"

Three holding screws.

3/8"

2BA or 3/16"

3/4"

13/16"

1/8" ø

Thread 2BA or 3/16" whole depth.

3/16" sq. silver steel.

1 1/4"

Hole 1/8" ø.

This section 1/2" long.

Thread 1/8" x 40 TPI. 2" long. Recess for ball bearing.

3/32" ø ball.

Scribers 1/8" ø x 1 1/2" long. Silver steel, harden and temper.

Holes and screws 5 BA. or 1/8".

1"

1/2"

5 BA.

scribers but the construction of it enables it to be opened considerably larger than any dividers possibly could be. As dividers are also used for scribing circles and arcs, it follows that the trammel will also enable us to do much larger ones of these as well.

The first trammel I ever made was so heavy that it was an effort to lift it. It worked all right, and in fact was remarkably efficient. I stopped and asked myself if I really needed so much bulk, and the answer was no. The result is the one seen in the photograph, and if it bears resemblance to those in tool catalogues then it is highly probable that I have been influenced by them, even though unintentionally.

Basically the tool is a simple turning and drilling job. We start with the two main pillars which are made from 1/2in. diameter mild steel, although there is really no reason why brass or aluminium would not do as well. The steps and grooves are turned on for fun, as is the knurling – all that is needed really is to drill a 1/8in. diameter hole in one end, and a tapping size for about 3/16in. in the other. I used 2BA but it could just as easily be anything else of about that size. One then has two holes for the screws drilled in it and the other just the one as can be seen.

The pieces are then set in a machine vice, at right angles to the screw holes, and drilled through ³⁄₁₆in. which will have to be squared for the bar. The one with two screw holes has a clearance hole drilled underneath, and again it needs to be about ³⁄₁₆in.

So far we have done a considerable amount of cross drilling, and this of course can be awkward. The easy way is to make up a jig, as described by Ian Bradley. I made up some of these some forty odd years ago and still use them regularly. However, we do not all have facilities for milling "V" grooves, and if a jig cannot be made up, then ordinary cross drilling will be required.

With the piece in the lathe, scribe a line across the end with a sharp pointed tool. Keep the chuck from revolving, or moving in any way, either by locking it or tying it with string, and then continue the scribed line made with the tool down the piece to the place where the hole is to be drilled. We now have a mark for the drill to enter the work, and a mark across the end where it is to go to give us a guide.

Put the piece in the machine vice, or "V" block, with the place where the drill is to go through as near to the top as you can manage. Touch it with a revolving centre drill, and check that it is exactly on the line. If not, revolve the piece in the vice and lightly try again. When it is right, make a reasonable indentation with the centre drill. Then use the drill and start to drill lightly. Stop the machine, hold the drill bit down on the work, and look at it, getting your eye level with it.

It should be possible to see from the line scribed across the bottom of the work whether or not the drill is central. If it is then you are a better man than I am, because I always get it wrong first go. Slightly turn the work and try again, keep doing this until you can see that the drill is absolutely right. If you use a light touch you should be able to try about twenty four different positions, at least. My record is about forty.

Once the drill is lined up correctly, start drilling but don't go too far before checking again. Remember to use the line scribed across the work as a guide. When it is right, drill through. The piece with the two screws will also need to be drilled across. It should be possible to leave the work in the machine vice for the second hole, but don't take it for granted that because the first one is right the second one will be as well. It, too, will need the same procedure but probably less alterations.

The third piece can be made up in the same way. When the holes are tapped is a matter for you. Personally, I like to tap the small ones early. The principle being that I should break a tap, and need to start again. I will not have gone too far because, if I complete a job except for the tapping and then break a tap, I am inclined to say bother. Of course, in theory you should not break taps, but one never knows and as I don't

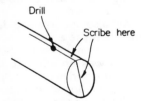

To cross drill a round bar scribe lines as shown. Use line across end as a guide.

*The finished broach. This can be pushed through the round hole to make it square.*

like work anyway I certainly hate wasted effort.

The three square holes are the next to tackle, and there are two ways of doing this. You can file them square with a needle file, a job which is not too time-consuming, or you can made up a drift. All that is needed for the drift is a piece of silver steel that is square and to the same measurements across the flat as the bar that is to be used. It has a series of grooves filed in it, with the edges relieved to make cutting faces. Do not go too deep.

The photographs were made to show what it should look like but the grooves are too deep in one; it was done this way so that it would show up in the photograph. Start the grooves off with small hacksaw cuts and then file them out with a three square file. Harden and temper to a dark straw colour, just possibly turning to light blue. If left too hard it will break easily. Touch the edges up with a small oilstone before use. In use it needs a series of light taps, and then withdrawing, rather than trying to force it through in one go.

The scriber points are the same as I have described earlier, so no further description should be required. The screws that secure the points are commercial ones, but the ones at the top and the one for adjusting will have to be made. I made up a length of studding for the adjuster and stuck the knob on with Loctite. It would have been more professional to have made it as one piece. The groove in it is to take a ³⁄₃₂in. ball bearing and should be about ¹⁄₃₂in. deep. In use the trammel is set to size, as near as possible and then final adjustment is made with the screw adjuster.

# Drill Clamps

Drilling metal can be a somewhat risky operation if one does not take reasonable care. Among the potential dangers is the possibility of work being snatched up in the drill if not properly secured. Clamping work to a drilling table without the proper equipment can be a time-consuming exercise as it is difficult to get it set accurately with the normal methods using clamps, nuts and bolts. Not only does the work tend to shift as one or other of the bolts is tightened but the webs under the drill-

ing table which are there for support always seem to be exactly where one wants to use the spanner to tighten things up. A machine vice can be used for smaller work that is to be drilled, but even here if the vice is not held securely the power of the drill will be quite capable of moving it on the table, and if it snatches then we not only have the work flying round but the vice as well. The little clamps I am about to describe seem to obviate most of these problems, and I find that they can be left

*The finished clamps. While making a pair, bits for further ones can be prepared.*

*The top bar, seen from above and below, and the bottom plate with adjuster in place.*

1½in. or 40mm wide. In fact it can be a little wider if you happen to have some material lying around. Cover it with marking fluid and, using odd-legs, scribe a line along the centre lengthways. Mark off and drill and tap two holes at 2¼in. or 55mm centres. Use a hefty tapping size – I have suggested ⅜in. or 10mm. In point of fact one of these for the actual clamp could be made a clearance size. I tried it and it worked but I found adjustment easier with the hole tapped.

most of the time on the drilling table and will not get in the way. I use two but of course if you feel at some time like making some extras then they will always come in handy. The sizes given work with most machines but it may just be possible that some people will have to modify things for their own purposes. This is not difficult once you get the idea of how they work.

Basically the clamps consist of a base or bottom plate, a top plate or clamping bar, an adjuster and a clamping screw. The bottom bar is made from a piece of mild steel plate (either black or bright will do) and it should be at least ³⁄₁₆in. or 4mm thick. It can be a little thicker, but not too much or it will sometimes be difficult to clamp small work. The metal is specified as 3in. or 75mm long and

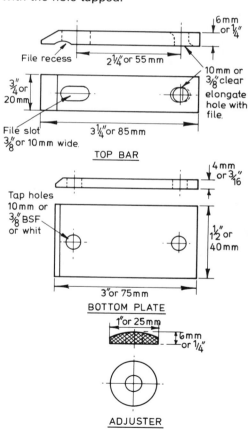

31

*The two clamping screw bars, the longer for beneath the drilling table.*

The top bar is 3¼in. or 85mm long, and I have suggested ⅜ × ¼in. or 10 × 26mm mild steel strip. Once more after the marking fluid has been applied scribe a line centrally along it. It now needs marking-out for three clearance holes for the tapping size used in the base. Two need to be drilled so that the edges are just touching each other, and the third drilled at 2¼in. or 55mm from the place where the two previous holes

touch. The two holes close together are then filed into a slot, leaving the other one at the correct distance from the centre of that slot. The third one then needs to have a round file put through it at an angle, so that the hole no longer is at a right angle but at about sixty degrees. The filing action will also open it out sufficiently to allow some adjustment when the clamp is tightened up. Finally we need a slope filed on the end

*Left, action of the clamp when gripping thin work – note shape of bars.*

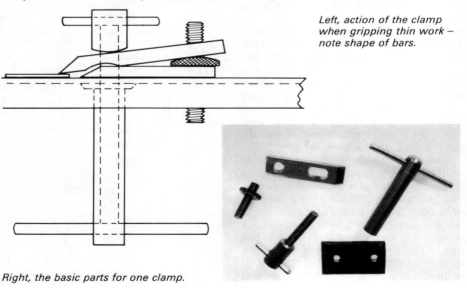

*Right, the basic parts for one clamp.*

of the top bar and a groove as shown filed at the point where it meets the base. The latter is to allow it to lower right down to the drilling table to hold very thin work.

The table clamp which goes underneath the table needs to be long enough so that you can get at it without actually fiddling about under the table. I have suggested 3¼in. or 85mm. It needs to be drilled and tapped to about half its length and the other half can be drilled clearance size. There is no reason why it should not be tapped full length, except that no doubt swarf would work its way up and into the threads, and also the friction would make it a lot harder to work with. When it is completed it can be cross drilled for the cross bar. Remember that the bar must clear the bottom of the table for the clamp to work properly.

The work clamp is a shorter version of the table clamp but as there is no need for any clearance section it can be threaded all the way. It might be an idea to make the tommy bar in two halves so that the threaded rod will go right through and this could be done by securing the two parts to the main

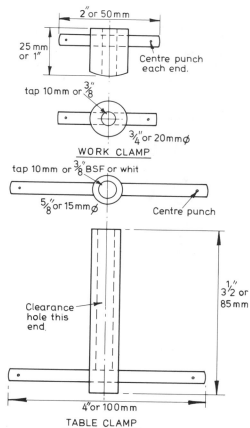

WORK CLAMP

TABLE CLAMP

clamp with a good retaining compound. The bottom part of the clamping screw is rounded so that it will accommodate the clamping bar at an angle.

The adjusting nut is a straightforward drilling, tapping and knurling job. One end, though, again needs to be rounded off as it will be resting on the clamping bar which will be at an angle. The best way to deal with it is to drill, tap and knurl in one operation and then before

*A finished clamp ready for use.*

is why the adjuster is there. The studding on the clamp itself can be run into the table clamping screw until there is just enough left to get a good torque with the work clamp. A sloped edge on the base combined with the groove in the top bar will allow thin work to be clamped direct to the table if one so desires. At the same time by winding out the studding on both clamp and adjuster quite thick work can be accommodated. The clamp should be used to secure machine vices when these are in use, and if small vices are being used then a third clamp holding the moving jaw in position as well as the two holding the clamping lugs works absolute wonders.

taking the metal from the chuck round it off with a small form tool, then part off. If you do not fancy parting off, saw through the bar while it is in a vice, protect the knurl with pieces of card at each chuck jaw, and face the end.

All that is required now is two suitable lengths of studding, and these can either be made or they can be the commercial variety. The rear part of the clamp should always be raised with the adjuster to be slightly higher than the front when it is used, and this of course

*A single clamp used to prevent movement of a machine vice.*

# Filing Plates

You may look through all the tool catalogues you wish but nowhere will you see filing plates listed. Indeed I do not even know if that is what they are called. They are little devices much used by skilled craftsmen to enable tiny work to be held in position whilst various operations are carried out on them. The name "filing plates" is one that I conjured up but I suppose that as they can be used for other types of work then there must be other more suitable names that could be applied to them. Holding tiny work, even in a very small vice, is extremely difficult, but by using a couple of pieces of scrap plate tiny objects can be secured with little difficulty. Here I will suggest several versions, but a little thought will enable you to adapt the plates to any object being worked on, no matter how awkwardly shaped it is.

There is one common factor running through the whole range, and that is the base on which they are made. It consists of a piece of plate about ⅛in. or 3mm thick, and about 1in. or 25mm wide. It will need to be about half or twice as long as it is wide. There is no set measurement and any odd bits of metal can be used for the purpose. Riveted or screwed to this plate is a piece of square bar of the same length or slightly shorter. The bar can be anything between ¼in. or 6mm and ½in. or 12mm square. Its sole purpose is to enable the plate to be clamped firmly in the vice when work is being carried out. From here we can now develop the filing plates.

The first type is merely a tiny stepped clamp for holding small flat pieces in position. Two holes are drilled through a small piece of steel bar, say ⅜in. or 10mm by ¼in. or 6mm. The bar is then held to the plate in the desired position with cyanoacrylate adhesive and the holes continued through the plate, and the bar riveted to it if need be. The top

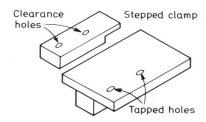

Clearance holes    Stepped clamp

Tapped holes

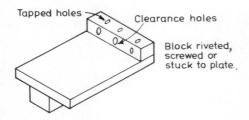

Tapped holes

Clearance holes

Block riveted, screwed or stuck to plate.

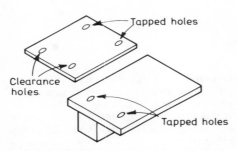

Tapped holes

Clearance holes

Tapped holes

bar is removed and the holes in the plate tapped. I usually use 5BA or 3mm for the purpose but anything near that will do. The holes in the clamping bar, as it has now become, are then drilled out clearance size and a suitable step filed on the bar. When the bar is screwed down work can be firmly held underneath it. An alternative method which will give more pressure is to drill only one hole in the filing plate and then to tap the hole furthest away from the step in the clamping bar. Putting a screw in that will tip the clamp forward and put extra pressure where it is needed at the clamping end. I find anyway that my plates end up with lots of holes after a time as I put different fittings on them, so probably both types of clamping can be incorporated on the one plate.

For certain operations on tiny round work a square bar the same size as that used for clamping can have a number of different sized holes drilled along it to take different pieces of round metal. Above each of these a small tapped hole enables a screw to be inserted to tighten up on the round piece. The square bar is then screwed to the plate. It is now possible to pass the round lengths through the holes and work on the ends as one wishes.

A simple flat plate slightly smaller than the filing plate with matching

*This filing plate has a series of tapped holes. A threaded rod or screw put in these can be worked on as required.*

*This filing plate is made for work on round bar.*

clearance holes to two holes tapped in the main plate and two other tapped holes at the other end allows one to secure thin sheet metal firmly.

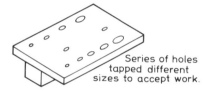

Series of holes tapped different sizes to accept work.

A series of tapped holes along the plates allows for screws to be put through when one needs to shorten them or possibly file a step on them.

If a hacksaw cut is made along the length of a plate with the hacksaw held at a forty-five degree angle whilst so

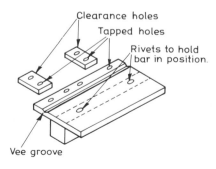

Clearance holes
Tapped holes
Rivets to hold bar in position.
Vee groove

doing then we end up with a small vee block. Two tiny clamps made up in the method previously described and you can work on the top of tiny round bars and tubes. This one is particularly useful for soldering to small round pieces.

The final one I have shown is slightly more sophisticated and the clamping device consists of three parts. First is a fixed stop which can be both screwed and held with adhesive to the plate as it

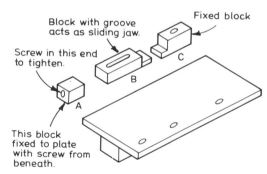

Block with groove acts as sliding jaw.
Fixed block
Screw in this end to tighten.
B
C
A
This block fixed to plate with screw from beneath.

is the part that will support the work. The second part has a small slot through which a screw passes into the main plate. This makes a moving jaw. The third part is again fixed and has a screw passing through it parallel to the main plate: this acts like the moving vice jaw

and allows tightening up on the work. In the example shown a small step has been made in the "vice jaws" but this was mainly to suit the particular purpose for which it was being used and there can be all sorts of variations. For example a small vee at right angles to the main plate will enable round work to be stood upright.

I am sure readers will by now have the idea and will later realise how useful these things are. Make up your own clamps to suit the job in hand, and as I have already suggested several different devices can be incorporated on one plate if you wish. Clamp making does not have to be limited to cutting and filing. Sometimes if you wish to hold a peculiarly shaped piece of work then a suitable piece of metal can be silver soldered on to provide the odd shape you wish to get. Likewise work held in them can be machined as well as worked on by hand.

# A Small Hand Clamp

This little tool can be made in virtually any size one wishes and is yet another means of holding small work whilst carrying out operations. The addition of a handle means that a good firm grip can be obtained while work is being carried out. It also means that the work can be held free of a vice or other bench clamping device, which is a requirement we often meet when model making. The tool can also be used as an aid to soldering by adapting the gap at the front to suit one's own purpose. No measurements are given for the tool as sizes will depend on the individual use to which it is to be put. Quick to make, it is the sort of tool which I find tends to be made on frequent occasions for various purposes with the result that in

the end the toolbox contains a number of them in a variety of sizes.

The working parts of the clamp consist of a flat plate as a base with a heavier section on the top to act as the actual clamp. I find that I invariably use square material for the main body, as I will call it. In fact the use of square stock is not necessary and any suitably-sized material will do. The base needs to be a little wider than the main body, and both will need to have two holes drilled in them in order that the screwed rod used to tighten the clamp can be passed through. My method of doing this is to stick the body to the base using a good cyanoacrylate adhesive. In fact for such purposes these days I invariably use Permabond C4. This is not by any

*A selection of small hand clamps.*

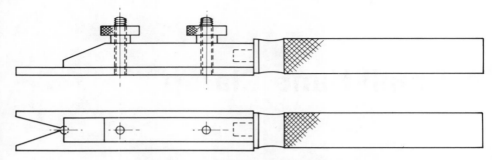

PLAN SHOWN WITHOUT SECURING KNOBS

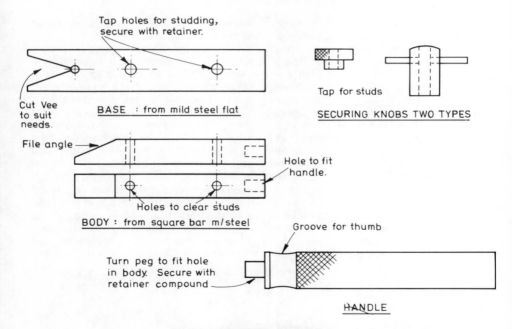

Tap holes for studding, secure with retainer.

Cut Vee to suit needs.

BASE : from mild steel flat

Tap for studs

SECURING KNOBS TWO TYPES

File angle

Hole to fit handle.

Holes to clear studs

BODY : from square bar m/steel

Groove for thumb

Turn peg to fit hole in body. Secure with retainer compound

HANDLE

## SMALL HAND CLAMP

means the only suitable adhesive but I find it easy to obtain and it allows time to adjust the parts before it sets. Once the adhesive has been allowed to set then I find I can work on the metal as I like and the parts will not separate until I slightly heat them. The parts should be stuck so that one end of the body comes level with one end of the base, it being central along the length of the base.

This means that there is a slight overlap of the base at each side and a larger one at one end.

The next job is to put some form of marking fluid on the top of the body. I use a spirit-based felt-tipped pen as a rule for little jobs such as this, as it is easy to apply from the pen. However, that is a personal preference and any marking fluid will do. Once this is dry, scribe a line along the centre of the body. The use of odd-leg calipers will do this for you and if you do not have any then they are another easy thing to make. On the line, make two centre punch marks for the holes. Here again the choice of position is yours, but do not get them too close together or too near the front end. Too close together will mean that you will have difficulty manoeuvring the clamping nuts and too near the front end will sometimes make sighting the work you are doing difficult.

Drill right through the two parts using the tapping size drill. The size of thread chosen must be a personal choice but it should not be in diameter more than one-third the size across the body nor less than one-eighth. Ideally about a quarter seems to work out about right, but as the idea is to use whatever material is to hand then there must be flexibility. Make a slight centre punch mark on the top of both the body and the base. This is so that you will know which way up they were when you drilled them. Then take off the burrs and separate the pieces. This can be done by just heating them slightly, but do not breathe the fumes when you do so as they are toxic. While there will not be enough gas given off to do any serious damage it can give a throat infection. It is possible to separate the parts without heat by holding the body in the vice and

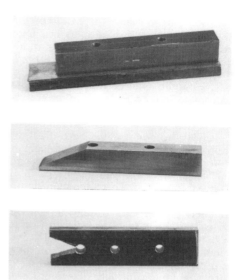

*Top, the square bar is drilled, then stuck to the base and the holes drilled through. Centre, after separation an angle is filed on the clamping block and (bottom) a hole is drilled in the base and a V-notch sawn.*

giving the base a sharp hard blow sideways. Before doing so put a piece of hardwood between the work and the hammer to prevent damage. If you try to use soft wood you may well end up with the work buried in the wood!

The base can now be tapped to whatever size you are going to use, while after cleaning off any surplus adhesive the body can be put in the four-jaw chuck and, after centring, a hole drilled to take the spigot on the handle. The two holes through the body can then be opened out to a clearance size for the thread that will pass through them. Do not make this clearance too tight as there is a danger of the clamp binding, so make it just a little bit sloppy. A typical example would be if a 2BA stud was being used then $3/16$in. would be the clearance size; add $1/64$in. to this and you will be about right. If you are metricated and using, say, a 6mm thread, then use a 6.25 clearance drill.

The handle can again be any suitable diameter or length. If the diameter is too large then you will not be able to lay the whole clamp flat on the table or bench, if too small it will be difficult to hold, so try for a good compromise. Put it in the lathe and turn the spigot to go in the body. This needs to be a push fit that will not bind. The adhesive manufacturers suggest two-thousandths of an inch but as I personally am never quite certain what size hole my drills will make, I turn the work until I can push it in and out but feel it binding slightly on the sides of the hole. Next turn the little rounded recess for the thumb grip. This is best done with a round-nosed tool. I find that with a well-rounded tool I can go to a certain depth at each end of the recess and a fraction more in the middle and end up with a nice smooth groove. It takes a little practice but it works.

Next we need to put on the knurl. Grip the handle in the chuck and only knurl for about two-thirds of the length, working from the thumb groove. The reason I suggest this is because I have found that handles knurled over the whole length tend to be rather rough on the hands. A smooth section at the end prevents this. When the knurling has been done turn the work round, putting a piece of cardboard between it and each chuck jaw, to prevent marking your nice faultless piece of knurling. Then turn the smooth part down just enough to come below where the bottom of the knurling would be if it had been continued. We are in fact talking about a gnat's whisker. Round off the

end to make a nice part that will fit into and not chafe the palm of the hand. It is as well to do this by facing across in a series of small steps and finishing with a small form tool. Such a tool is well worth making as it will be used very frequently during your career in model engineering.

The two studs can either be made by threading lengths of material of suitable size or by using lengths of commercially-made studding which is remarkably cheap. If you make your own then there is not really any point in threading the part which will be covered by the body when the clamp is closed. A suitable length of thread on each end will do.

The clamping knobs can again be made from any suitable-sized material. One way of making these is to put a length of material in the chuck and knurl it for a suitable length to cover two knobs. Centre drill, drill and tap with a taper tap for the length of one knob. Turn a step as shown and then part off. If you do not like parting off saw it off and later you can face the end. The second knob is a repeat of the first. When both are done run a plug tap through to make sure the thread is clean. A second type of knob can be made by drilling and tapping a suitable piece of bar. Then cross drill it and put in a small piece of rod to act as a tommy bar. The rod can be held in with a retaining compound and I use Permabond 168 or Loctite 638 for this sort of work. A third alternative is to use commercial wing nuts. Again they are ridiculously cheap for what they are and very effective, allowing one to get a great deal of purchase when tightening up.

It only remains now to put the slope on the front of the body. This can easily

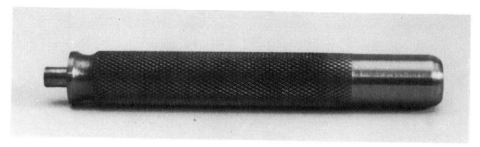

*The clamp handle, ready for securing the body.*

be sawn and filed. If you have a milling machine then the temptation will be to use that, but I doubt if it will be as quick as sawing and filing, unless you are making a batch of them. To make the vee at the front scribe a mark where the body ends on the base after being put onto the studs. Centrally on this, make a centre punch mark and drill a small hole. Then saw at an angle from the front, after marking out where the saw cuts are to be. Do not be tempted to leave this bit of marking off, as it can be difficult to get the vee angle accurate unless there is a guide. Clean up the saw marks with a file. Last but not least secure the handle to the body with our old friend Permabond 168 and allow it time to dry, and there you have your clamp.

I have never had any problems about using retainers to secure the handle to the body, since I discovered there was such a substance available. However, if you are not too confident of getting the clearances right for the retainer then the body can be tapped and a suitable-sized thread turned on the handle spigot to allow it to screw in to the body. I made my early clamps in this manner. Try to vary the size of the vees in the ends of the bases as this will allow a variety of work to be carried out. A wide vee will frequently allow intricate filing operations to be carried out in a piece of sheet metal, while a narrow vee is better for working on the surface of sheet or on small metal rods and bars.

# Pin Chucks

Pin chucks are used to hold tiny drills. When the drill is held in the pin chuck it can be put into a larger chuck or a special holder. If the small drill was put straight into the ordinary chuck, there would be a good chance that it would not be possible to tighten the large chuck up sufficiently to obtain a grip.

If a knurled shank is put on a pin chuck then it becomes a pin vice. A pin vice is used for tapping very small holes, as well as sometimes for drilling tiny holes by rotating the drill by hand. Apart from the knurled shank there is no difference in the two types of tools. Many commercially-made pin chucks and pin vices have interchangeable collets. There is no reason why this should not be done by the home constructor as well but it is far easier to make a number of different tools to cover the range that will be required.

*Top, the finished chuck with, above, the two parts required.*

The chucks anyway will hold a range of sizes. They do not require much metal or expertise to make.

The main body is first of all put in the lathe and drilled from the rear end with the large clearance hole. Turn the work round and thread it to take the cap. Drill a small hole for whatever sized drill you

*The pin chuck described (centre) with two commercial examples.*

*A commercial pin chuck with separate collets for various drill sizes.*

will need the tool for. Make sure it breaks through to the clearance hole in the other end. Move the top-slide over and turn the taper as shown on the drawing. Do not at that stage re-set the top-slide.

Before making the cap a taper reamer will be needed. Just turn down a piece of silver steel using the top-slide as set for the body. File a flat to half the diameter of the silver steel and harden and temper to light straw.

The cap can be made at one setting apart from the outside taper, which is there only for appearances. It requires drilling to three diameters. One is for the thread, with a slightly larger one to just clear the body. It will then need to have a short length drilled to the lowest

diameter of the taper on the main body. This one will go right through the cap. When it is drilled use the taper reamer to finish it off as shown on the drawing.

*Top, the simple home-made taper reamer. Above, a very small pin vice in aluminium which has given good service for many years.*

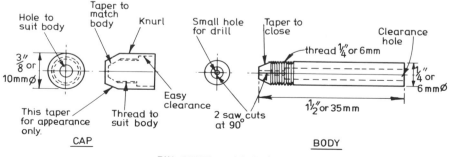

PIN CHUCK: mild steel

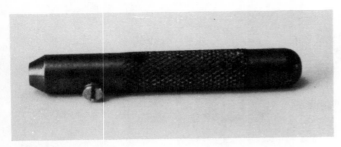

*The simplest form of pin vice, a knurled brass rod with a through hole and a radial grub screw to secure the drill.*

*A double-ended commercial pin vice which allows several sizes of drill to be used. Note use of hex. rod. This is excellent as a handle for needle files.*

Finally while still on the setting put a small knurl on it, and part it off.

It is now just a case of turning the cap round in the chuck and putting a slight taper on it, as I have already pointed out purely for appearance. It is probably as well, though, to use the top-slide setting already in use. All that then remains to be done is for a fine saw cut to be put along the thread in the main body. A hacksaw blade, even the Junior type, makes too wide a slit. A piercing saw will do nicely, or it can be done mechanically with a slitting saw if one is available. One cut will do but two at right angles if you can manage it would be even better.

When the cap is screwed on the hole should tighten up as in a normal chuck. The only reason it is unlikely to do so is if the thread on the body is not quite long enough. The remedy then would be to lengthen the thread a little. If a pin vice is required then a fine knurl on the main body will convert the pin chuck for you.

# Toolmaker's Clamps

There are many types of patented clamps on the market, most of which are extremely good as well as some being quite ingenious. However, in spite of this the humble toolmaker's clamp which has been available for many years still is one of the best methods of holding work in position. The construction of it is such that a considerable torque can be put on when it is tightened up. It also allows a certain amount of adjustment to be carried out on the material immediately prior to clamping it; it is probably the only clamp that allows this.

Toolmaker's clamps can be purchased in a wide varity of sizes, but are somewhat expensive. At the same time they are remarkably easy to make and all sorts of odds and ends of material can be used to produce them. In spite of this, when I visit people's workshops I am often quite surprised at the way many of them improvise clamping facilities when they do not have sufficient clamps of the right type. Shortly before writing this I paid a visit to a modeller and he was trying to hold two sheets of metal together with 'G' clamps. Of course each time the clamp was tightened the work twisted out of position. In the time he spent trying to carry out the clamping operation he could have made a couple of toolmaker's clamps from the contents of his scrap box and got the job done in half the time!

A toolmaker's clamp consists basically of two identical bars of metal joined together with a pair of screws. The rear screw is tighted up first so that the clamp is lightly resting on the work. If the front one is then tightened the clamp will lie parallel, giving a very rigid clamping action.

Three types of clamps are shown, the first of which is the normal commercial type that can be purchased. The first variation is very useful as it stops the situation where a longish length of the adjusting screw projects on either side, an arrangement which can be awkward in certain situations. The third one is an entirely different type of clamp that leaves a flat top surface when tightened up, again a useful arrangement in some situations.

To start with we will need two pieces of metal bar of the same length. The bar should preferably be square but if flat material is available in your scrap then it will do. It will obviously need to be

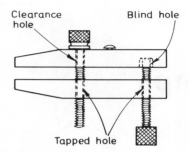

Clearance hole  Blind hole  Tapped hole

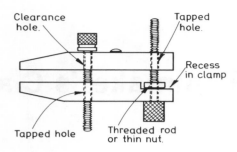

Clearance hole.  Tapped hole.  Recess in clamp  Tapped hole  Threaded rod or thin nut.

thick enough not to bend under pressure. As the clamps can be made in a variety of sizes no measurements are given but the length of the metal bars should be anywhere between seven and twelve times the thickness. So if we are using ½in. or 12mm square bar then the lengths should be between 3½ and 6 inches or 84 to 144mm. The ideal ratio I suppose is about seven or eight, but the longer ones can sometimes have their uses.

Mark out the first bar ready to drill two holes. One hole should be about a third of the length of the metal from the end, and the other about the same length from the other end as the thickness of the bar. Both holes will need to be centrally placed along the bar. Drill them with a small drill which will act as a pilot. File off any burrs and then stick the two bars together with a good cyanoacrylic adhesive. Drill through the hole a third of the way along into the other bar and right through, and just make a recess in the other one about a third of the bar thickness.

Open out the holes so that the two holes in the one bar are tapping size. The hole in the other one will need to be drilled clearance size, and the recess will also need to be opened out to

clearance size. At this stage the bar with two holes can be tapped. The other one will need a third hole drilled in it to take a screw to hold a clip which prevents the adjusting screw from moving about. This will need to be a smaller size then the adjusting screws and should be about halfway along the metal bar.

We now need two adjusting screws. These can either be turned down and threaded or a commercial studding can be used and the knobs held in position with retaining compound. The threads used for this purpose should be about a third to two-thirds the width of the bar, so with a 15mm bar we would need a thread of 5 or 10mm, or better still somewhere in between.

The knobs are simply turned to size, drilled, tapped and knurled. One needs a small groove cut in it. This groove takes the securing device for the clamping screw. If very large clamps are being made then it may be as well to drill a cross hole in the knobs to allow a small tommy bar to be put in for tightening purposes.

The little clip for securing the front screw can easily be pressed out from thin metal. A simple press tool or jig is made up as shown in the drawings. A thin metal strip can be put in this and

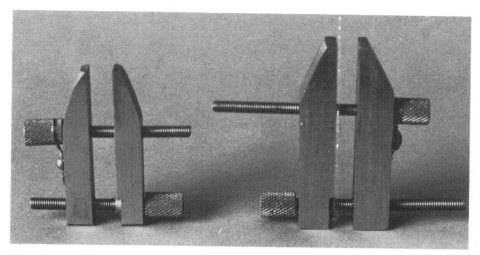

*Two clamps of the second type described. In each case the clip holding the adjusting screw in position has been made from bent up wire.*

when placed in a vice and tightened up it will take up the required shape. An alternative is to twist up some wire as shown and use this. It will need to be put in the groove of the knob before twisting and then just wrapped round a piece of metal rod of the same diameter as the securing screw in order to get the loop which the screw will pass through.

Finally the front of the clamp should be tapered off. This operation is useful rather than essential. It gives a better view of the work when using the clamps. The amount of taper is purely a personal choice.

The second type of clamp is similar to the first and I do not propose to describe the whole operation of construction. Instead of two holes on one bar being tapped, one on each is opened out for

*The third type of clamp. Note the extra length left on one end to allow it to be fixed in the vice if required.*

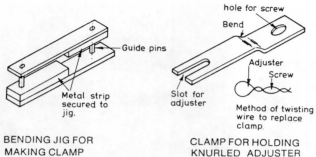

BENDING JIG FOR
MAKING CLAMP

CLAMP FOR HOLDING
KNURLED ADJUSTER

clearance and the other tapped. These are at opposite ends on each bar. A small recess is filed in one bar as shown and a thin knurled nut is made up and fitted to the adjusting screw. This prevents it sliding about. It should be secured with a compound such as nut lock. Take care when doing so that the thread does not get stuck in the threaded hole. I find this type of clamp of considerable use.

To make the third type we come back to the two tapped and clearance holes being on the same bar as we had in the first case. This time a recess is either milled or turned in the bar with the clearance holes in it and a knurled nut made up to fit in this recess. It is possible to leave the tapped bar slightly longer than the other one on this clamp. This then allows a means of securing the clamp in a vice if need be.

To adapt the clamps to hold small round stock tiny vees can be filed in the jaws as shown in the drawing. This too is a useful trick as otherwise round stock has a tendency to roll out of the clamp during tightening operations.

ADAPTATION OF
STANDARD CLAMPS
TO HOLD
ROUND STOCK

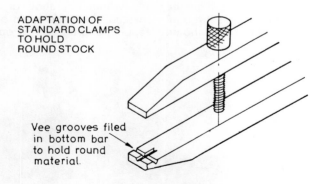

Vee grooves filed in bottom bar to hold round material.

# Tap and Die Holders

As each year passes, the standards set in model engineering reach new heights. This not only applies to the very fine exhibition models that we see at Wembley and other large exhibitions, but also to Mr. and Mrs. Average who these days always seem to be looking for an improvement in their own humble efforts, and are constantly struggling to reach new standards. More precise modelling inevitably means the use of smaller nuts and bolts with the associated problems of how to make tiny threads of say 12 BA or below, or of a fraction of a millimetre. What is needed is minute equipment with which to use the necessary taps and dies and these notes are an attempt to help those wishing to make the smaller threads to do so with as few frustrations as possible. There are two problems associated with the making of these threads. The first is handling the tools, and the second is how to get the threads square. The latter is not by any means confined to small sizes. Without some sort of aid I am very capable of putting even a very large thread in a piece of metal at an

*The finished miniature tap wrench and a 12 BA tap (on a matchbox!).*

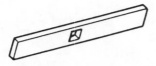

*The simplest wrench of all. A metal bar with a square hole.*

angle when it is meant to be square. The tools described will, with a little adjustment to the measurements, serve equally well for larger sizes as well.

## THE TAP WRENCH

Putting even an 8BA tap in a normal small size tap wrench is a dangerous proposition. The wrench makes the set-up so top heavy that even the slightest wobble will cause the tap to break. In such circumstances, small wonder that the thread ends up out of square. The Eclipse chuck type does help quite a bit, particularly at 6 to 8 BA. When we start getting to twelve and below, even that becomes cumbersome because of the extended length. What we need then is a miniature wrench which, combined with our guides, will lessen the chances of that fatal wobble.

Tap wrenches are among the easiest of tools to make and probably the easiest way of all is to take a piece of flat steel, say ⅛in. by ³⁄₁₆in. and about 1½in. long. Drill a small hole in the centre, file it to a square to fit the square on top of the tap with which it is to be used and a tap wrench is yours in about ten minutes flat. One snag! Unless you are very lucky you will find that each tap has a different size square on the top and a different wrench is needed for each one. Still, if we think about it, it is not really too much of a snag as, with the tool costing next to nothing and taking no time at all to make, why not have one wrench for each? Why not go even further? Put each end of the two pieces in the four jaw chuck, turn them round and a very neat little tap wrench indeed will be the result.

The idea of the simple wrench is in many ways perfect. Perhaps, though, you want something that looks a little more professional. In this case take two pieces of the same metal, each about 1¼in. long, drill and tap them as shown and when they are screwed up with the tap between the two screws you have a small tap wrench suitable for a variety of sizes. Once again if the ends are turned round a nice looking little tool will be the result. The tool has taken probably less than an hour of your time. There is really nothing at all wrong with

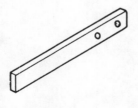
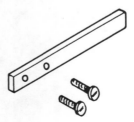

*A simple tap wrench. Two metal flats screwed together. The square of the tap fits between the screws.*

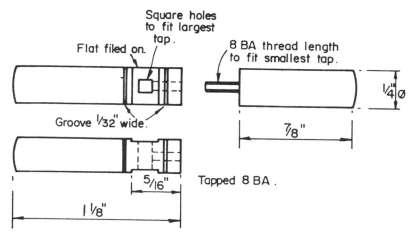

Square holes
to fit largest
tap.

Flat filed on.

8 BA thread length
to fit smallest tap.

Groove 1/32" wide.

Tapped 8 BA.

either of the two types described above and I do not know to this day why I decided that I wanted something that looked a bit more professional. Vanity probably. I wanted my friends to say "Coo, that's nice, where can I buy one?" I also decided that I was going to make mine from stainless steel. As far as the tool is concerned stainless steel has absolutely no practical advantages whatever over ordinary mild steel. Two things swayed my judgement on this. Firstly, for months I had about two inches of the right diameter stainless steel alternately lying on the bench or the floor. When it was not doing this it was being picked up off the floor. I wanted to get rid of it but it was too

*Using the miniature tap wrench with a tapping guide to maintain a ninety degree thread.*

*The tap wrench compared with a matchbox.*

metric equivalent, both are 1⅛in. long. The first piece is simply turned down for ¼in. and threaded 8BA. Make sure the shoulder is nice and square. 8BA may seem a little small but six is too large and I doubt if many readers will have seven. The metal was then turned round in the chuck and the other end rounded off by the highly technical means of filing. Ideally a small form tool should be used but for my purposes a file was good enough. No knurling is needed in this size as, with small size taps, the less pressure exerted the better. The other end was then faced, drilled and tapped to take the first piece. A cross-hole was drilled of a suitable diameter to just clear the flats on the largest tap to be used. When I say largest tap, this does not necessarily mean the largest diameter thread, so much as the largest square, as it is quite probably that a 12BA tap will have a thicker shank and larger square than even an 8BA tap. I found that the shanks of my taps below 8BA varied from 2·8 to 3·3mm and the squares likewise. The hole now has to be filed square with a needle file and it should end up a snug

nice-looking to throw away. The second thing was that instead of burning the midnight oil in the workshop I had been watching too much television and had been fascinated by those highly polished tools used by surgeons when they were doing transplants. If you want to use stainless OK, it looks nice, but if not stick to mild steel.

Making the wrench is very easy and is ideal for a beginner. Two pieces of steel are required, both ¼in. diameter or the

*The tap wrench with four tapping guides.*

fit on the largest tap. This means that the smaller ones can be held by the screw while the large one will hold in on its own. At this point some adjustment should be made to the male thread as of loss of concentration occur (such as the blonde next door appearing in the garden topless), which can result in a sudden jerk breaking the tap. The guides are made from mild steel on the princi-

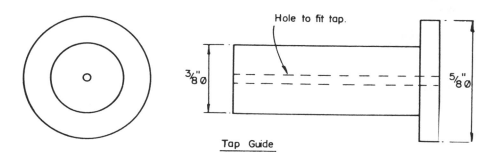

**Tap Guide**

it needs to just nip the smallest tap without leaving any thread protruding. 8BA is not very large and we want as much torque on the main body as possible, rather than on the thread. I then filed on two flats as shown in the drawings and, with my surgeon's in mind, put in two small grooves. Neither of these operations helps the operation of the tool but it makes it look nice. The same high precision method as before was used to round off the end.

## TAPPING GUIDES

It is, as I have already explained, remarkably easy to put even quite a large tap in at the wrong angle. In the small sizes we are talking about, getting one in out of true can mean disaster. The guides, which are a simple turning job, prevent the tap going in wrong and protect it when those awkward moments

ple that surgeons do not use tapping guides. A number are made with holes through them to suit the various shank diameters of the taps, and of various lengths which again suit the different lengths of taps. There is no reason why they should not consist of a piece of steel turned square at the ends with a hole through, except that I have found that the lip helps one to hold them in position. In use they are simply put over the hole and support the tap which is passed through. They can be held in place for some jobs with one of the weaker Loctite products such as Nutlock and a sharp tap will release them when the job is finished.

## THE DIE HOLDER

Here again, when dealing with tiny threads the standard type of die holder is far too cumbersome and will lead to

*The die holder showing the die in position. The three holes for securing the guide can be seen.*

inaccuracy. A standard tailstock die holder will do the job, but not always can the thread be put on with the work in the lathe. Also provision is made for this holder to be held in the tailstock chuck, and by doing so it is possible to make studding. This is not very easily done with a tailstock chuck, as the metal tends to bend and so only short lengths can be made at a time. The use of this dieholder enables several inches of small studding to be made under power

*The finished holder with a guide fitted.*

when used with the guides, which automatically correct any tendency of the material to bend. It is made of aluminium to reduce weight, working on the principle that the lighter it is, the less the chance there is of it being top heavy. There are no long arms, as with such small threads no great leverage is required, and the knurled grip is usually sufficient when threading off the lathe. A hole is provided for a small tommy bar if such a thing should be needed.

Start by turning down the small diameter at the top of the holder, reverse the work in the three jaw chuck, gripping it by the outside, not the part that has just been turned down. Run in a small centre drill after facing the metal and put a drill right through that will clear the threads to be made. Mine was a 1/8in. diameter hole but a smaller one would do. I next ran an end mill of 1/2in. diameter into the metal for about 1/4in. This is to make a start for the die recess and, ideally, if a 3/4in. diameter cutter can be used it will save a bit of turning. The recess was then turned to size and once again I had to measure dies, as not only were there slight variations in diameter but also in width. The recess will have to be made deep enough to take the largest one to be used, plus 1/8in. to accept the guide. It can be turned without starting with an end mill but the end mill helps sort out the square corners, besides saving quite a bit of time. The next job is to take out more metal on the face, leaving the outside lip which needs to be an exact 1/8in. as the accuracy of the guide will depend on it. We now need to just face across the lip 1/32in. deep. Do not take the work out of the chuck. Cut a piece of wood of a suitable size for the chuck jaw to rest on and be parallel to the bed. A centre punch mark is now needed and I

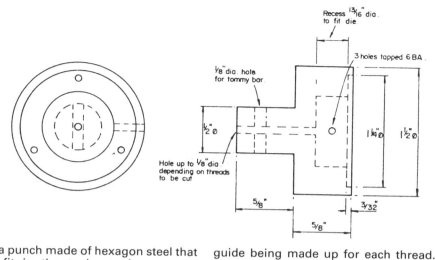

Recess $\frac{13}{16}$" dia. to fit die

$\frac{1}{8}$" dia. hole for tommy bar

3 holes tapped 6 BA.

$\frac{1}{2}$ Ø

Hole up to $\frac{1}{8}$" dia depending on threads to be cut

$1\frac{1}{4}$" Ø    $1\frac{1}{2}$ Ø

$\frac{5}{8}$"    $\frac{3}{32}$"

$\frac{5}{8}$"

use a punch made of hexagon steel that will fit in the toolpost. Any sort of pointed tool will do and it may even be possible to use a centre punch in a boring bar hole. If you possess some other means of indexing, then obviously the wood will not be required. When the three centre punch marks have been made the work can be taken out of the chuck and drilled tapping size for the screws. The knurling on the outside can be done with a tool such as that described later in the book. The only thing left to be done is to centre punch and cross drill the hole for the tommy bar. Start with a small drill, then you can see if it is not going straight, and can adjust it with a larger size. At the same time, drill and tap the hole to secure the die.

## DIE GUIDES

The making of these is a repeat of the turning operation of the die holder, the lip in this case being recessed. The hole through the centre is clearance size for the thread that is to be used, a separate

guide being made up for each thread. To get the three locating holes it will probably be as well to drill through the die holder enough to spot the guide on one hole and then drill. Assemble the

*The die holder showing the tommy bar to allow hand work to be carried out. If the tommy bar is removed the holder fits in the tailstock chuck.*

57

guide to the holder and screw it up. (At this stage the holder should have had the three holes tapped.) The one screw will hold things together and the other two holes can be spotted and drilled in the same way. There is no reason why the guide should not be indexed in the same way as the holder if you wish. The slight loss of accuracy that is likely to occur is of no real consequence as the clearance holes can be drilled slightly oversize, the accuracy of the location of the guide to the holder being by means of the lip rather than the screws. The screws themselves are ordinary commercial ones although the ones I used had larger than normal heads.

These simple tools will be useful in many ways but in particular you will probably wonder how you ever managed without the tap and die guides. They are very useful in all size threads and it is worth considering making them up in larger sizes. In the case of the die holder, if being made for large threads the tommy bar can be dispensed with and arms put on each side, being either screwed or brazed into the holder body which should, for larger sizes, be made in steel.

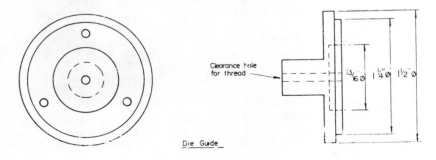

Clearance hole for thread

$13/16\ \emptyset$  $1'4\ \emptyset$  $1'/2\ \emptyset$

Die Guide

58

# Flycutters

It is difficult to imagine trying to work on a lathe without using a flycutter. It can be used for so many jobs where a flat surface is needed and it will always give such an excellent finish to metal providing care is taken, particularly with the finishing cut. The types of cutter described here were used initially to machine the casting of a large angle plate. I always use one when machining the port faces on cylinders, they can be used for machining coupling rods, and in fact have so many applications that it would be impossible to list them all in this book. While I am concentrating on the description of a flycutter for use on the faceplate of a lathe, once the basic idea has been grasped then there is no end to the variety of types you can make. They will also work well on a mill-

*The finished flycutter in use on the faceplate.*

*The finished flycutter.*

and the cutter remains in a horizontal plane. To make the simplest type of flycutter we simply make a device to hold a cutting tool on the faceplate. We then secure it so that when the faceplate is rotated the diameter of the circle created by the cutter is larger than the area to be machined. If the work is then slowly traversed the cutter will take a single cut at each rotation, or possibly a cut at each end of the work at some places. Because the cutter is often on or near the edge of the faceplate, there is a tendency for it to cause balancing problems. We therefore make two identical cutter holders, but forget to put the hole for the cutter in one. This can be bolted on the opposite side of the faceplate and will act as a counterbalance.

As not all readers will have the same size of lathe, I have as usual given relative sizes. The lathe faceplate will have slots in it and the cutter holder will need to be relevant to these: the bolts holding the cutter should be the same diameter as the width of the slots. Making them smaller will mean that the cutter will tend to move, whereas it must be held rigid on the faceplate.

Both types of flycutter merely consist of a short length of metal bar, capable

ing machine, or with a milling attachment, and I will explain later the small differences required for cutters for those purposes.

Let us ask ourselves what a flycutter is. I have always found that if I know what a tool is for and roughly how it is to be used then construction of it is easier. What in fact we are doing when flycutting is rotating a cutter while the work remains rigid, as against normal lathe work where we rotate the work

*A simple flycutter (centre left) with its counterweight and bolts to secure both.*

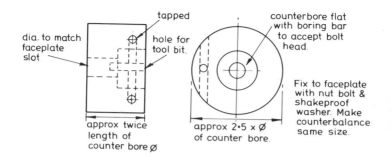

tapped

dia. to match faceplate slot

hole for tool bit.

counterbore flat with boring bar to accept bolt head.

Fix to faceplate with nut bolt & shakeproof washer. Make counterbalance same size.

approx twice length of counter bore ⌀

approx 2·5 x ⌀ of counter bore.

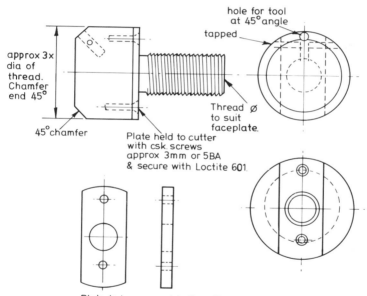

approx 3x dia of thread. Chamfer end 45°

45° chamfer

hole for tool at 45° angle

tapped

Thread ⌀ to suit faceplate.

Plate held to cutter with csk. screws approx 3mm or 5BA & secure with Loctite 601.

Plate to be secured to fly cutter.
Mild steel plate of suitable size & thickness.

of being bolted to the faceplate. A hole is drilled for a cutting tool and another is drilled and tapped for securing screws to hold the cutter in position. If a chamfer can be turned on the bar then it makes a better cutting angle for the tool. The first cutter shown has a hole drilled through the centre, which is counterbored to take the head of the bolt being used. This counterboring is best done by drilling a suitable diameter hole and then flattening the bottom

with a small boring tool. Don't forget you will need two of these pieces, and of course two suitable nuts and bolts. On one piece when the hole has been bored drill a suitable-sized hole for the tool. Anything between ⅛in. or 3mm and ⅜in. or 10mm will do, depending on the lathe size, but the larger the tool diameter that can be incorporated without weakening the holder the better.

To drill the hole for the securing screw can be tricky for those who have

*Using the flycutter to machine an angle-plate. Note counterweight.*

never done such a thing. The way to do it is to centre punch the place where it is to be, then drill to the depth of the drill point at right angles. After that turn the work round and you will find that the drill will go at the required angle from this initial drilling. The securing screw should if possible be about a third of the diameter of the tool bit, and it is sometimes an idea to drill and tap right through so that a screw can be put in both sides of the tool, making it extra-secure.

The second type of flycutter shown on the drawing has a shank turned on it and threaded instead of a bolt passing through. In many ways it is the most convenient method, but sometimes one does not have a die of suitable size where the thread will be of a large diameter, in which case of course the first type is the better one to make.

You will see that I have suggested putting a flat plate on the back of the second type of tool. If you have a milling machine then a flat could be milled on instead. The reason for the flat part is to prevent the cutter moving round when in use. It is not an absolute necessity but it does give the tool that much more strength. The plate will not of course be needed on the counter-balance you make for the opposite side.

If you turn the spigot on the second type of flycutter, and neither put a flat on the back or thread it and do not put the plate on the back, we have a cutter suitable for use in a milling machine, or lathe chuck. There is not a great deal of advantage putting one in the lathe chuck as it gives rather a large over-hang, leading to vibration. Also the cutter will only describe a comparatively small circle which limits the cutting area. In the milling machine this is not important as the table can be moved in two directions which gives full coverage. When using flycutters do not take too heavy a cut as it will cause rather a lot of wear on the machine. Keep the tool as sharp as possible, and the finishing cut should be as light as possible.

# A Rose Bit

Sometimes we need to use the lathe to make parts in small quantities rather than singly. The way to do this is to work either to stops specially made on your own particular lathe or to use the graduations on the slide handles. If there are several different operations to be carried out on each part this can be difficult, as either we have to change tools for each one or perhaps take the part from the chuck while we use the particular tool that is set in the lathe. For example, suppose we need to turn a round section to a smaller diameter, with a nice square collar, and then we need another part of the material turned with a radius, we will need two tools, a knife edge and a rounded one. We can get the use of one extra tool by actually turning one of the diameters from the tailstock, and it is for this we need a rose bit.

A rose bit is only a tool with a hole down the centre and with cutting edges round the hole so that when rotating metal is pushed against it the cutting

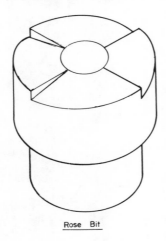

Rose Bit

*The rose bit in use, reducing the end of a length of hexagon brass bar.*

edges reduce the metal in size whilst the metal that has been so turned passes into the hole. The only disadvantage to the tool is the fact that it does not give a very good finish to the turning unless very carefully made. If, however, a thread is to be put on the part that has been turned this is of no importance whatever. The die will tidy things up.

To make the tool, chuck a piece of silver steel. The diameter will depend on the finished size you want your job to be, but as a rough guide I would suggest three times the diameter. So if you want to turn the work to 5mm then you need your silver steel 15mm diameter. Having said that there is no hard and fast rule to the thing and you could certainly use 20mm diameter and possibly get away with a piece as small as 10mm. Drill a hole right through the silver steel which needs to be no more than an inch or 25mm in length. Put a larger drill through for about three-quarters of the length to allow clearance

as the metal passes through, otherwise it is likely to bind up and seize. At the same setting turn a square-edged step on it. The step is to allow it to push up against the tailstock chuck jaws for support.

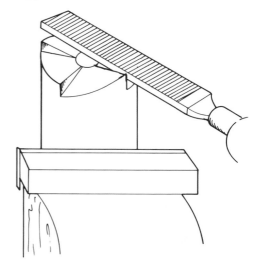

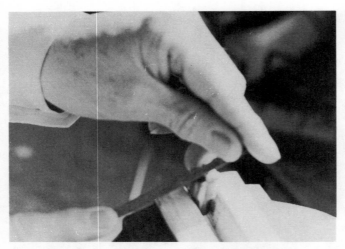

Put the steel in a vice and mark the end with the larger diameter into four even sections. File each section to an angle as shown in the drawing. In order to get each section at exactly the same angle a mark will have to be made round the circumference of the silver steel as a guide to the depth to which the file should be taken. It is as well to leave the marking of this mark until you have some idea of where it will be needed, and I find that this will sort itself out when I file the first angle. An easy way to get the mark is to wrap a piece of masking tape round the steel — it can be taken off when you have finished and it is easier than trying to scribe a line. When the angles have all been filed on, polish the edges with emery paper.

The tool will now need to be hardened by the usual method of heating to the colour of a boiled carrot and quenching in cold water. It must then be cleaned up and tempered to a light straw colour. Once again soaking in washing-up liquid before heating can save discoloration and make tempering easy. When it is hardened and tempered sharpen the edges with a small slipstone that has been well oiled.

To use the tool all that is needed is to put it in the tailstock drill chuck and make sure that the tailstock will not slip. Leave as little overhang on the barrel as possible and then wind the tool against the work which is rotating. The work will slide up the rose bit which will also act as a steady. A different bit can be made for each job and a small wooden block with a series of holes drilled in it will make a nice stand for a set of tools that increases in size as you go along.

# Box Tool

A box tool is another means of turning from the tailstock. It is somewhat more sophisticated than the rose bit, and gives a cleaner finish. As nothing comes free there is a penalty to pay: it is more difficult to make and is much bulkier. It does have one other advantage, though, and that is the fact that you do not need a different tool for each diameter. Also, a round shoulder on the work is possible if required.

In order to get the greatest accuracy it is best if the tool is made with a taper to fit your tailstock. At first this seems a somewhat daunting task, but as long as you have a top-slide that will turn at an angle it is a fairly simple thing to do. Put a piece of round bar in the lathe chuck and centre drill it. Put a centre in the tailstock, and another between that and the metal in the chuck. I am assuming two things here, firstly that your centres have centre marks in the ends and secondly that you have two tapers to fit the tailstock. Some lathes have a different taper in the head, and of course that

*A box cutter with Morse taper shank.*

67

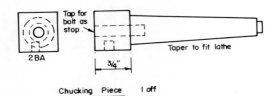

Tap for bolt as stop

2 BA

Taper to fit lathe

¾"

Chucking Piece    I off

taper will not work. If you do not have the two matching tapers then the tail of the tool will have to be made parallel to fit in the tailstock chuck. The arrangement will work quite well but gives rather a lot of overhang which might lead to chatter.

Back to our two tapers lined up between the tailstock and the metal in the chuck. Set up either a clock gauge or a simple little indicator with a spring pointer and turn the top-slide round until when you move it up and down the centrally-suspended taper the needle of the clock or the pointer of the indicator remains steady. This means that the top-slide is at exactly the correct angle to turn your taper. Do not be tempted to get it near enough. It must be right. It is surprising how much a taper will vary if

it is the tiniest fraction of a degree out. Having got it right then it might be an idea to turn several tapers for use at a later date if required.

When the top-slide is set put a suitable sized piece of square bar in the lathe chuck, and turn the taper on it. The length of the taper must be the same as those for your lathe. It will mean for most readers hand feeding and there is a temptation to feed too fast in these circumstances. Take it easy and you will get a good finish. Rush the job and the taper will not hold in the tailstock. When you have your taper right, turn the metal round and drill and tap the square bar. The hole is for a stop and the thread size is not important. Finally you will need a hole drilled and tapped across the square to take the screw that

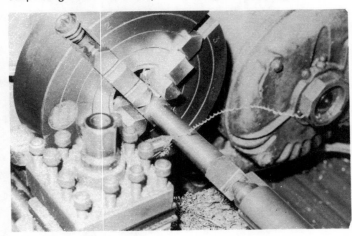

*Turning the Morse taper.*

All holes 2 BA clear.

Tool and Steady Guides
2 off

holds the rest of the tool in position. Measurements are given on the drawings and they are about right for lathes with Number 2 Morse tapers. For smaller sizes they need to be reduced in proportion. I would suggest half the size for Number 1, fifty percent bigger for Number 3, and for Number 0 about one-third.

*Photo above shows a box tool in use.*

We next need a plate of about ⅛in. or 3mm thick. Mark it out and drill it as per the drawings. To be mounted on this are two identical blocks. One takes the cutting tool and the other a small

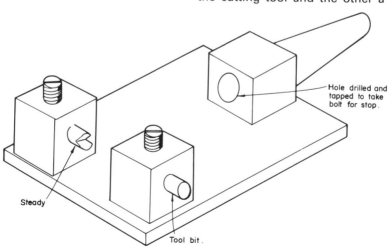

Hole drilled and tapped to take bolt for stop.

Steady

Tool bit.

69

*Two versions of the box tool, one with Morse taper for tailstock fitting and the other for a turret or chuck application.*

steady. Note that the steady hole is in advance of that for the tool. It is just simply a case of cross drilling each one and tapping one hole for a securing screw on each. This hole goes right through, one end taking the screw that holds the block to the plate, the other the securing screw for tool or steady.

The cutting tool is made to a standard cutting tool design, from either high speed steel or silver steel hardened and tempered to a light straw colour. The steady can be either a piece of plastic rod or, if you cannot get hold of anything suitable, a piece of brass will do. Actually the plastic rod may well be found in the form of a sprue in a plastic kit. It will need to be turned to the correct diameter but the material is nice and soft and ideal for the purpose.

When assembling, the taper will have to be held with a screw and retaining

compound spread on the square blocks. This is to prevent it moving out of line when in use. If you do not want to do it this way then secure it with two screws instead of one. The blocks holding the steady and the tool could be dealt with similarly, as there is also a possibility of these turning out of position when in use.

To use the device, adjust the cutting tool to take the required depth of cut, bring the steady up to meet the work and adjust that too. Simply wind in the tailstock and the tool will take care of the rest. The screw near the taper can be used as a stop so that if several cuts are being taken there is no need to worry about stopping the movement in the right place, the work will stop when it reaches the screw. Obviously that screw must have a flat head on it to make it work properly.

# Knurling Tools

I believe that a knurling tool of one sort or the other is absolutely essential for the model engineer. If your interest is in tool-making then it is hard to think of many tools that do not both look and function better for knurling some part or another. If your sole interest is in making models then perhaps the need is not quite so great but nevertheless at some time or another you will want to knurl the edges of a handwheel or some similar object. The tools are somewhat expensive to purchase while being com-

paratively simple to make, and they well repay the little time it takes to construct one. The tool can be no more than a bar with a slot in it and a wheel in the end, or the slightly more efficient but also more complicated caliper type. The advantage of the latter is that no strain is put on the lathe bearings when the tool is used.

Knurling wheels can be purchased at any good tool suppliers. They come in a variety of sizes and patterns and you must decide what pattern you want on

*Two caliper-type and a single-bar example of knurling tools. Single-bar has a straght-cut wheel but the alternative diamond is at the side.*

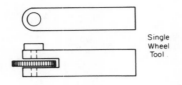

Single
Wheel
Tool

your work before purchasing. If you are making a single wheel tool then it is possible to purchase both straight and diamond pattern knurling wheels, and it is also possible for a tiny knurling tool to use the striking wheel sold in tobacconists for cigarette lighters. These are ridiculously cheap but these days only seem to be sold in a sort of fine diagonal pattern. Even so I still use them for very fine knurling and the finished result can look very attractive indeed. For the caliper type of knurling tool then two wheels will be required: they are sold left- and right-handed. They can be obtained as fine, medium or coarse and it is up to you to decide which will suit you best. It may be as well to settle for medium if one pair is all you are going to have, as a finer knurling pattern can be obtained by not

digging the tool in too deep, although this gives a rather flat pattern which would be somewhat criticised by professional toolmakers. The obvious thing is to get a fine and a medium pair and make two tools, which saves the bother of trying to change wheels each time you need a particular pattern and the tools are easy enough to make anyway.

Let us start with the single wheel type of tool. All that is needed is a piece of square steel bar to fit the toolpost of your lathe, and long enough to protrude about an inch or 25mm when it is clamped in that toolpost. A hole to take the pin that is going through the wheel is drilled across this bar at the end that will protrude from the toolpost. It should be at such a distance from that end that when the wheel is on it the edge will extend by some $^3/_{16}$in. or 4mm.

The next thing to do is to cut a slot in the end for the wheel to recess into. This can be done by drilling a hole at a suitable distance at right angles to the one you have already drilled and then sawing down the metal until you reach the hole. Do this at each side and the

*Using a slitting saw to cut the notch in the arm.*

piece of metal will fall out, leaving the slot just requiring a clean up with a file. A more sophisticated way of getting the slot is with a small slitting saw. These are sold by good tool merchants and come in a variety of thicknesses and diameters as well as having a variety of hole sizes. It is certainly worth while investing in one as they can prevent you having to do a great deal of hard work. They seem to last for years and years and are far more accurate than the sawing and drilling method.

If you have settled on your slitting saw then you will need to mount it on a mandrel. For those that do not know the name, "mandrel" is a technical term for a bit of round bar with a nut or bolt on the end. True, the bar wants to be slightly more elaborate than just that, but not very much. What is needed is a piece of mild steel of about twice or

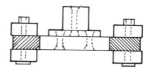

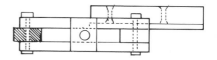

CALIPER KNURLING TOOL

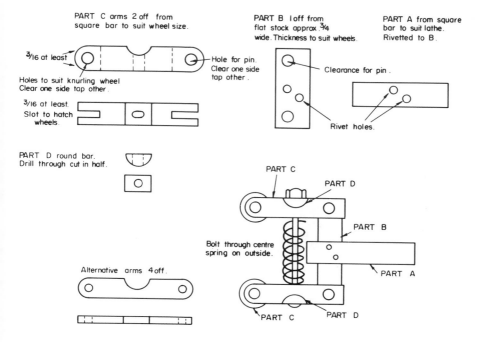

PART C arms 2 off from square bar to suit wheel size.

PART B 1 off from flat stock approx. ¾ wide. Thickness to suit wheels.

PART A from square bar to suit lathe. Rivetted to B.

³⁄₁₆ at least

Holes to suit knurling wheel Clear one side tap other.

³⁄₁₆ at least. Slot to hatch wheels.

Hole for pin. Clear one side tap other.

Clearance for pin.

Rivet holes.

PART D round bar. Drill through cut in half.

PART C

PART D

PART B

Bolt through centre spring on outside.

PART A

Alternative arms 4 off.

PART C     PART D

three times the diameter of the hole in your slitting saw. Turn a short piece down so that the saw just goes over it with no play and if possible with the saw just slightly overhanging the edge. Drill and tap through the end with a tap about half the diameter of the hole. Screw in a short bolt with a washer, and your mandrel is made. You may well find that the saw blade has a keyway on it. Do not worry about this, It is meant for use on horizontal milling machines. Providing you use the saw sensibly it will not slip round. It is of course possible instead of drilling and tapping the mandrel to turn another short length at the end and thread that and use a nut and washer. Each way the end result will be the same.

Before we get round to using the tool one further tip. The mandrel may have to be used in the three-jaw chuck, unless you have a set of collets. Three-jaw chucks are rarely true and this will mean that if the saw goes back in a different position then the error can be doubled and it will end up describing an arc instead of a circle. If you lightly centre punch it by the number one jaw, then each time you put it back it will go

in the same position and save a lot of problems. Even better still make the mandrel from hexagon material and centre pop the flat at number one jaw, there can then be absolutely no error whatever when the mandrel goes back and it should run perfectly true.

When using a slitting saw do not run it at too fast a speed. Do not feed it too fast and do make sure that you use plenty of cutting fluid. If you do all these things it is possible to make cuts to the full depth of the saw. However, run it too fast and dry and in no time at all the teeth will disappear and anyway the maximum depth of cut will be very small indeed. The work can be mounted either on the cross-slide or in the tool-post for sawing. Make sure it is clamped well down and you will wonder how you ever managed to work without a slitting saw once you get the hang of things.

Now let us get back to our knurling tool. We should have a bar of metal with a slit in it and a hole crossing that slit. You will now need a pin for the knurling wheel. This should be of bronze and it is made with a plain flat head as narrow as possible. The shank must be just the right diameter to fit the hole, and a thread will have to be put on the end for a nut to hold it in position. Quite a straightforward little turning job. The reason bronze is specified is because the knurling wheels are diamond hard. If you use mild steel, or even hardened silver steel, the wheel will cut right through it, but it will not cut through bronze. Bearing surfaces should always be made of different materials: using the same material for each component is asking for trouble. There is another way to deal with the situation and that is to use a steel pin and a bronze bush. The hole in the metal bar is drilled

*Left and right-hand knurling wheels showing the small bronze bushes fitted to reduce hole diameter.*

*The small caliper knurling tool.*

smaller than that in the knurling wheel and a small bronze bush made to fit both the knurling wheel and the pin. Do not put the bush in the wheel with a retaining compound, but try to make it a nice push fit. If you use a retainer and it wears you will never get it out to replace it.

That, then, is all there is to the single wheel knurl. To use it you just wind it in to the slowly-rotating work and when the pattern starts to appear wind the top slide very slowly along in the required direction. There is a lot of strain involved in knurling so take it easy and use plenty of cutting liquid. If the knurl does

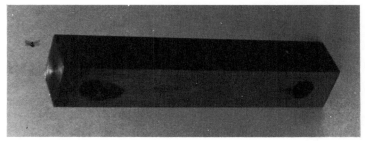

*One of the caliper arms drilled ready for slotting.*

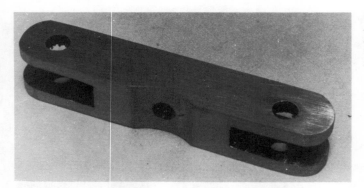

*One of the arms slotted, rounded etc. and requiring only the centre hole to be slotted for completion.*

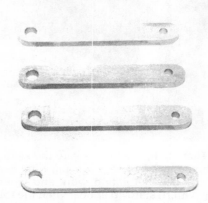

*An alternative to solid slotted arms is to make them from separate pieces.*

not appear deep enough go back and start again. Providing you do not rush putting the tool in the wheel will feel its way into the original pattern.

At last we get to our two-wheel type of tool. Fortunately much of what I said for the single wheel type applies here. Start with the part shown as A on the drawing, a simple square or flat bar of metal to fit your particular tool-post. Part B is also a flat piece of mild steel. The thickness must be the same as that of the knurling wheel, i.e. if you have ³⁄₁₆ in. wide knurls use a ¾-in. by ³⁄₁₆-in. piece of metal. Part B needs four holes drilled in it. Those at each end are for the arms and the others for riveting to part A.

Part C can take two forms. The best type is for the parts to be made of

*The half-round parts D are cut from bar. Two adjusting screws are also needed.*

*Using the caliper knurling tool.*

suitable square bar with two slots cut in with our slitting saw, and a hole in the centre opened out into a small slot. The other alternative is also shown and this is to make four arms from, say, ⅛-in. or 3mm thick mild steel and mount these either side of part B. The second arrangement works, but is untidy and is not quite so strong as the original one. There is a half-round cut out of both arms and this must be matched to the diameter of part D.

Part D acts as a guide for the adjusting screw. It is made from a short length of round bar cross-drilled to take the adjusting screw and then sawn in half. It is there to rotate just a tiny bit as the tool is closed up.

The only other parts required are four pins as described for the single-wheeled tool, and I would suggest bronze bushes for this one rather than bronze pins. Part A is riveted to part B and parts C held to B with two of the pins. A suitable bolt and spring goes through D and C

and a nut on top allows for adjustment on the work. You can use a commercial wing nut if you like, or better still make the first job with the tool a nice knurled nut to replace the commercial one.

Use of the tool is similar to the single wheel type except that this one is brought to a position where both wheels ride centrally over the metal to be knurled. Tighten up the caliper as hard as you can and then start the lathe. Run it slowly. Tighten up the tool again while it is running, but make sure you keep your fingers away from the rotating chuck. You are looking to get the knurl to a point where there are no flat spots on the top of the pattern but no very sharp edges either. Experience will show you how. Once again the knurling tool is slowly drawn along the rotating work. The same applies as with the single-wheeled tool. You can go back over the knurl providing you close up the caliper slowly to give the wheels a chance to pick up the pattern.

# A Filing Rest

Filing work in the lathe when it is rotating is a habit definitely to be discouraged. It is a dangerous practice in many ways, but mainly because there is the obvious possibility of the file slipping and one's hands being caught on a rotating chuck. Then there is the possibility of a sleeve catching in the chuck and causing injury as it tightens up with the rotation. Apart from the danger to oneself there is a distinct possibility of damaging or destroying work with a file, as there is little control over the movement of the tool if the lathe is running.

Filing work in a lathe that is stationary is a different kettle of fish altogether. There are many occasions where such an operation is desirable, and unless you own a small milling head or similar item then I would go so far as to say that the operation is a necessity.

Getting work even and flat when it is held in a lathe is not an easy task, and if more than one flat needs to be put on a piece of work then it becomes even more difficult. We need some sort of guide for the file, and the headstock locked in the required position. The latter can be done by simply tying the

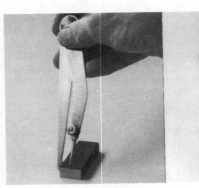

*Far left: after covering with marking fluid scribe a line along the centre with odd-leg calipers. Left, then scribe a line across the centre with calipers or a square and scriber.*

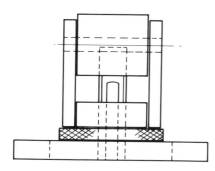

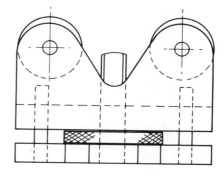

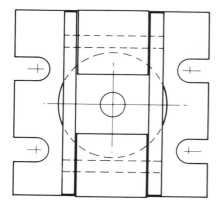

belt so that the mandrel cannot rotate. Getting the file level and flat can be done by the simple means of putting a piece of wood on either side of the work and using that as a guide. This works quite well as long as you have sufficient lengths of wood to be able to keep changing them as the height of the flat being filed gets lower and lower. Better still, therefore, is some sort of a rest that will allow a minute adjustment with the work as it is brought to the size required. If we can actually regulate this adjustment to the amount we require then that is even better as we can use it to

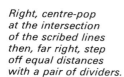

*Right, centre-pop at the intersection of the scribed lines then, far right, step off equal distances with a pair of dividers.*

*Place work in machine vice, start all holes with a centre drill. Follow with a pilot drill, smaller than finished size, then open holes to required size.*

measure the amount being taken off. The little rest that I am about to describe will do this for you, and although suitable measurements are given these can be altered in proportion to each other to suit individual lathe sizes as required. As shown it is suitable for the smaller type of lathe, but can also be used with larger ones either by making the base thicker or by using packing pieces underneath.

We will start with what I call the lifting plate. This is made from a piece of mild steel plate about 3/8in. or 10mm thick and 3/4in. or 20mm wide, although if you want a slightly wider rest it could be 1 in. or 25mm width. It needs to be 2in. or

50mm in length. The ends should be squared up and personally I prefer to do this in the four-jaw chuck, but filing will do. Coat with marking fluid on one of the wider surfaces and scribe a line centrally along it. In the exact middle make a centre punch mark and then, using a pair of dividers for marking off, make two more 3/4in. or 20mm either side of it. Drill all three 1/8in. or 3mm diameter and remove the burrs.

Next we come to the base and this is made from a piece of mild steel 2in. or 50mm square, and 1/4in. or 6mm thick. Using a good cyanoacrylic adhesive such as Permabond C4 stick the lifting plate centrally along the base, and

*The baseplate needs seven holes, one for the adjusting screw, two for guide pins and four for securing slots. Shaped plate with screwed rod in place is shown on left.*

when dry drill through with a ⅛in. or 3mm diameter drill. Separate the parts and open out the centre holes in each, the base to tapping size and the lifting plate to clearance. I would suggest ³⁄₁₆ in. × 40 or 6mm × 1mm as these give an adjustment that can be measured. However, if you do not have the right size taps then any ³⁄₁₆in. thread, British or American, or a 2BA will do. The odd thread numbers per inch will, however, make height measurement rather difficult. The base can now be tapped to the selected size.

The side plates can be of ⅛in. or 3mm mild steel, and one should be coated

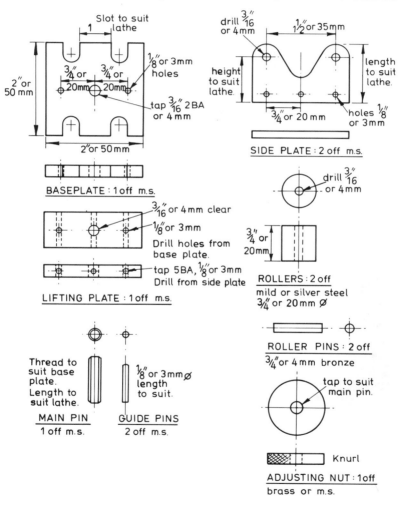

Slot to suit lathe

2″ or 50 mm

¾″ or 20mm   ¾″ or 20mm

⅛″ or 3mm holes

tap ³⁄₁₆″ 2 BA or 4 mm

2″ or 50mm

BASEPLATE : 1 off  m.s.

³⁄₁₆″ or 4 mm clear

⅛″ or 3mm

Drill holes from base plate.

tap 5BA, ⅛″or 3mm Drill from side plate

LIFTING PLATE : 1 off  m.s.

Thread to suit base plate. Length to suit lathe.

⅛″ or 3mm⌀ length to suit.

MAIN PIN
1 off m.s.

GUIDE PINS
2 off  m.s.

drill ³⁄₁₆″ or 4mm

1½″ or 35 mm

height to suit lathe

length to suit lathe

¾″ or 20 mm

holes ⅛″ or 3mm

SIDE PLATE : 2 off  m.s.

drill ³⁄₁₆″ or 4mm

¾″ or 20mm

ROLLERS : 2 off
mild or silver steel
¾″ or 20 mm ⌀

ROLLER PINS : 2 off
¾″ or 4 mm bronze

tap to suit main pin.

Knurl

ADJUSTING NUT : 1 off
brass or m.s.

81

*The side plates are stuck together with cyanoacrylate for drilling and machining.*

*After shaping the plates are separated and the roller pins retained in one ready for assembly.*

with marking fluid, then the five holes marked off as shown on the drawing and punched. Stick the two plates together and drill through all five holes with a ³/₃₂ in. or 2.5mm drill. Separate and remove the burrs. Next carefully stick one side plate either side of the lifting plate, and when dry drill through with the same drill. Separate and open out the three

The base of the filing rest fitted with adjuster and guide pins.

holes in the bottom of the side plate to ⅛in. or 3mm. Bolt the two plates together through these three holes and open out the two top holes to ³/₁₆in. or 4mm diameter. This should ensure that they are lined up properly.

Two rollers are now turned to size; they need to be bored to take the pins and faced off to length. There are two schools of thought on these rollers, one that they should be hard to prevent them wearing and the other that they should be soft to prevent the files wearing! Personally I feel that as they will rotate with the file they should be hardened and therefore make them from silver steel, get them to red hot (the colour of a boiled carrot) and drop them in water. If I was keeping them soft then mild steel would be my choice of material. Two pins will have to be made for them to run on and these are best made from bronze as this will virtually prevent wear. These pins will eventually be held in place in the side plates with retaining compound so they just need turning to length.

The rest is adjusted by means of a nut

which fits between the base and the lifting plate. It should be drilled and tapped and at the same time knurled. If using threads that allow measurement of height adjustment it may be as well not to knurl it but to divide it equally in four (using the chuck jaws if you do not have a dividing head) and drilling a small hole at each point of division, say ⅟₁₆in. or 11.5mm diameter. A small rod can be put in these holes to turn the adjuster round, and the amount of height movement gauged by their position. For example, if using a metric thread as suggested one complete revolution will lift the adjuster 1mm.

Slots must be put in the base, and these will have to suit your lathe. Ideally two slots are best as they make fitting easier, but one will do if this suits your requirements. The alternative is to drill holes in suitable places so that it will bolt to your cross-slide. Before finishing with the base we need two guide pins, which are just lengths of mild steel to prevent the rest moving sideways when being adjusted. These can be held in position in the base with Permabond 168 or similar retainer. We also need the screw on which the adjuster is to run and this is a plain piece of studding of the correct thread, held in again to the baseplate with the retainer.

Finally it is just a case of assembly and how this is done should be clear from the drawings. The lifting plate will of course need to be tapped to take the screws

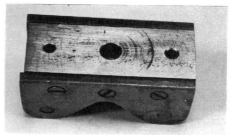

*The moving part of the rest from above and below. The marks show how the adjuster raises it.*

that go through the side plates, the side plate holes having been countersunk so that the screws do not stick out and get in the way. It is possible to make different types of rollers to take half-round or round files etc, but this is a matter of individual requirement. Once the idea is implanted variations become easy and a matter of personal preference.

# T-Bolts, Dogs and Jacks

Earlier remarks about noticing a shortage of proper clamping accessories when visiting workshops apply equally to the use of old bolts and suchlike instead of proper 'T' bolts. This is not good practice and without doubt all workshops should contain a complete set of clamping accessories suitable for use on every machine in that workshop. Even if the owner only has a lathe then there should still be a suitable range for that machine, and if he owns several then a set is required for each size of 'T' slot. The rich ones amongst us will no doubt rush down to the local tool stockist and purchase what they require. The humbler ones will want to make them, and they are the sort of job that can be done in odd moments.

'T' bolts themselves are quite simple. All we need is a piece of studding, either home-made or purchased. It is probably as cheap to buy studding as it is to buy the mild steel to make it. We

*Tee bolts. The two on the left were made by the author, the other is a commercial item by Myford Ltd.*

*Tee nuts made by the author. These are a very useful alternative to T-bolts.*

then need a suitable strip of mild steel, drill and tap a hole, secure it with Loctite 638, or braze it in, and you have a 'T' bolt.

They will be needed in various lengths, and I find that sometimes it is convenient to make them offset, with the studding nearer one end than the other. The strip of metal used as the foot must be a good fit in the slot, and the studding for your stock sizes should be of as large a diameter as possible. A slight chamfer on the leading edge will help the foot locate, but it must be very tiny.

So you can see that while having those odd half hours or so waiting for the wife to get ready when you are going out to dinner, slip into the workshop and make a couple of 'T' bolts. In this way you will avoid those nasty times when you want to set up a job, can't find the right clamping bolts, and so get rather despairing as it means taking the job off the machine to make some.

## 'T' NUTS

Another item well worth having is a set of 'T' nuts. Owners of many types of lathes will be familiar with these as they invariably hold the topslide in position,

Width and thickness to suit lathe.

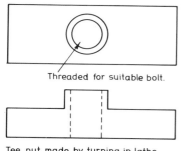

Threaded for suitable bolt.

Tee nut made by turning in lathe.

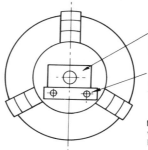

Short length of bar drilled in centre, with tee nut bolted to it.

Strip secured underneath. Prevents tee nut from turning.

Method for making tee nuts with very thin base in the lathe.

at least on most lathes. They require just a little more expertise to manufacture. For maximum efficiency, and to cause the least damage to the machine, they should be made so that the flat part is a good fit in the bottom of the 'T' slot, and the raised section is also a good fit in the upright part of the slot.

If you own a milling machine they can be milled to shape and then drilled and tapped. Or the work can be done the other way round. If not, they need to be turned. This is easy enough if you are making nice big ones, as it is just a case of putting a piece of square bar crosswise in the 4-jaw chuck and turning the boss, drilling and tapping at the same setting.

However, if you own a small machine such as the Toyo or Unimat, these 'T' nuts will need to be very thin and it is not so easy to turn them in one go. The best idea is to use a slightly thicker piece of metal than needed. Put it cross-

wise in the 4-jaw, turn the boss, drill and tap, leaving a much larger foot than required. Then put the round part, which you will probably need to make longer than required, in the 3-jaw chuck and turn the foot down to size. The extra length on the round section can be filed off.

There is another way of doing the job which is probably even better, and that involves mounting a piece of bar in the 3-jaw, or a piece of plate on the faceplate. Drill and tap it smaller than the hole will be in the 'T' nuts. Drill a suitable strip of metal for the 'T' nut and bolt it to the bar or plate.

Take the bar or plate from the lathe. Drill and tap it so that it can be used to secure a strip of metal to form a bar underneath the 'T' nut. This will act as a support and prevent the 'T' nut turning. You can now turn as many 'T' nuts as you need, and the little jig will probably be useful for other things as well. I have a piece of plate for the faceplate, with holes all over it, which has been used time and time again for such jobs. It is much easier than doing a lot of clamping.

## CLAMPING DOGS

Next we come to dogs. Not the canine variety, but the things we use on our 'T' bolts, to hold the work in position. These really only consist of a metal bar with a slot in it, the bar goes over the 'T' bolt, or round the bolt in the 'T' nut, and holds the work.

We can of course get just a heavy bar of metal and drill and file, or mill a slot in it and we have what we need. Such an item is somewhat cumbersome, and can be difficult to use. The end of the bar needs supporting away from the work as, in order to get the maximum

*A typical clamping bar with adjusting bolt. The inclusion of this bolt saves the constant search for packing when clamping work.*

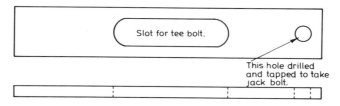

Slot for tee bolt.

This hole drilled and tapped to take jack bolt.

Clamping dog, with screw jack fixing incorporated.

pressure, the clamp should lean slightly downwards on to the work. Organising this frequently involves having a great number of packing blocks in order to obtain the right height.

This can be, to say the least, inconvenient and it is easier to make dogs with built-in jacks. Just simple strips of mild steel of suitable thickness with short slots filed in them for the 'T' bolts, and at one end a hole is drilled and tapped. A bolt is put through this with a locking nut and this is used to adjust the height. The bolt end should rest on a piece of brass to protect the machine. Once more, if the slot filed, on some of the dogs at least, is off-centre this will often facilitate getting them closer to the work where it needs to be secured.

Dogs can also be made that give a great deal of versatility from thin mild steel strip, say $\frac{1}{16}$in. thick. Four or pieces are cut, each $\frac{1}{8}$in. or so shorter than the other. A slot is filed roughly

An easily-made screw-jack which can prove extremely useful when adjusting work being clamped down.

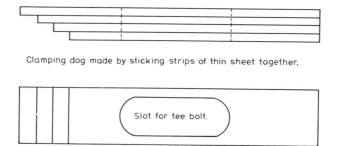

Clamping dog made by sticking strips of thin sheet together.

Slot for tee bolt.

Thin sheet metal steps to provide variety of clamping positions.

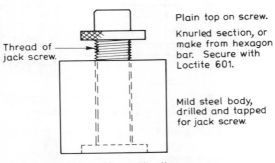

Thread of jack screw.

Plain top on screw.

Knurled section, or make from hexagon bar. Secure with Loctite 601.

Mild steel body, drilled and tapped for jack screw.

Recess at base fits other jack if required.

in each, measuring from one end. The pieces are now held together, using an adhesive such as Loctite 330 Multibond. The slots are then finished off as one, and the result is a clamp with a series of small steps in it, which can used either way up.

Packing blocks can be made in a similar way, and I have heard the use of washers suggested for this purpose. I do not personally like the idea of using them as there is not a great deal of support left for the dog, and quite a bit of pressure will be applied. But if space is at a premium the idea can be useful.

## SCREW JACKS

Finally we will need separate jacks for the situation where our normal dog with the built-in jack will not work.

These are simple screw devices, and again make a little project for the odd half hour or so between cups of tea. Several sizes should be made if possible, and the sketches will show how to make them. They can also be used for levelling off non-symmetrical items such as castings which have to be machined.

No matter how many of these various accessories are made there will always be some need to adapt. For example the use of straps (strips of metal with a hole either end for 'T' bolts) should be considered, this often being a good way of work holding. Even so, if sets of these various things are made up then it is surprising how much time can be saved when actually doing modelling and it is surprising, too, how much easier life in the workshop becomes.

# Boring Bars

In any workshop with limited facilities the only possible way of ensuring accuracy in boring is to bore between centres, but this appears to be a subject of which many people have heard but few have actually tried or even seen.

The normal method practised by model engineers is to put the work in the 4-jaw chuck, or on the faceplate, and to use a boring bar in the toolpost, or sometimes a boring head in the tail-stock. This is all right but inevitably there will be a certain amount of spring in the tool used in the toolpost and this can result in a tapered bore. It also means that the lathe work is limited by what diameter can be swung on the lathe. Boring bars themselves, in many home workshops, seem to be something of a hotpotch anyway, and whichever way you propose to do the boring it is as well to make up a decent set

*A between-centres boring bar used to bore a cylinder on a poppet-valve engine.*

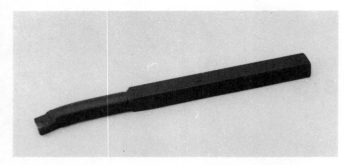

*A typical small commercial boring bar from cast steel.*

*A tool-holder that will hold an ordinary tool or a boring bar. The holder can be made to avoid the need for packing.*

of holders. Such a set will not take long and will amply repay the time taken. All we need is some suitable square bar material.

## BORING BAR HOLDERS

Select a bar to suit your lathe. Mount it in the toolpost and put a centre drill in the mandrel, using either collets, a drill

STANDARD BORING TOOL HOLDER.

Tool locking screw.

Hole for tool bit drilled right through.

Mild steel bar to suit lathe.

chuck or the 3-jaw chuck. After centre drilling, put in a drill of the size of tool bit you plan to use, drill through and the tool recess is done. Drill and tap for a grubscrew to secure the tool bit and you have your boring bar holder.

Make several holders with different diameter holes so that as the hole to be bored gets larger, the tool bit that is suitable can be used. The thicker the tool bit, the less the whip that will cause a taper. If the tool is ground to exactly half the diameter of the steel, then you are absolutely certain that it will be at centre height. High speed steel should be used for preference but silver steel has its uses too. When using high speed steel the bar will have to be set at a slight angle in order to clear the hole, if silver steel is used it can be bent, to give clearance.

## BORING BETWEEN CENTRES

For boring between centres we need a bar of mild steel of suitable diameter and, like the ordinary boring bar, several sizes are really called for. Centres are

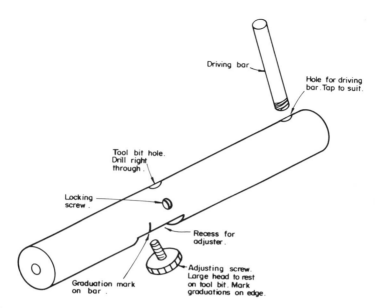

Driving bar

Hole for driving bar. Tap to suit.

Tool bit hole. Drill right through.

Locking screw.

Recess for adjuster.

Graduation mark on bar.

Adjusting screw. Large head to rest on tool bit. Mark graduations on edge.

marked and drilled on the ends and the bar is then turned between centres on the lathe thus ensuring it is absolutely true. A hole is now drilled across the bar to take the tool steel, and a hole drilled and tapped for a grub screw to secure it once it is located in position. If you like, it can be used with no more refinement than this, and all that it means is that every time the tool needs to be pulled out a little further, the distance it is from the bar is checked with a vernier slide gauge.

A little further refinement can be added, though, by filing or milling a flat on the bar at the point where the hole goes through. Drill and tap a hole next to it and make up a suitable screw to act as an adjuster by bearing on the base of the tool. The thread used should be a useful one, and if you are metric then one with a pitch of 1mm or 0.5mm should be used. You then known when the screw is rotated exactly how much

the tool has been moved by. I use forty threads to the inch as this gives me a nice micrometer reading. The large headed adjustment screw is divided up, and a mark on the boring bar shows where to locate the marks. The result is easy adjustment of the tool, without the need for constant measurement. The screw should be a full thread, and the hole tapped with a taper tap, to ensure that there is no possibility of the adjuster screw falling out when the bar is being turned.

In practice the work is bolted to the lathe saddle and is traversed up and down while the boring bar is rotating at a suitable speed; the result is a smooth and accurate bore. The usual way to rotate the bar is via the catchplate on the lathe striking the driving dog which is secured to the boring bar – on which a flat has been milled or filed to allow it to grip. The one shown in fact has a bar screwed into it with which to make

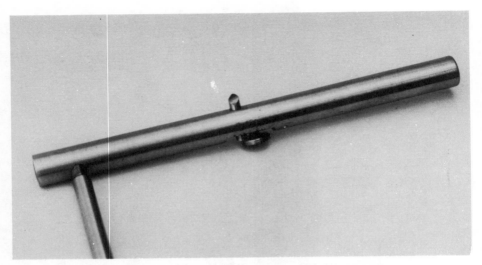

*The between-centre boring bar with screw-in drive dog and tool adjusting screw.*

contact with the catchplate, and this gives a much more positive driving action.

## HIGH SPEED STEELS

The tool is made from high speed steel, and a word or two about this may not come amiss. When one goes to the local shop or sends to the supplier for high speed steel, I wonder if the type is ever specified. Like all materials there are various grades of the steel and it is worth checking whether or not the grade you have is the most suitable one for the job. Eclipse list three grades, VH for use on extra tough steels, and this is possibly as good a grade as any for cast iron, H5 for cutting at high speeds and HM2 for normal cutting of mild steel and non-ferrous metals. So you

can see the latter is not the one to get if making locomotive wheels and similar items, or boring cast iron cylinders. Although designed for high speed cutting, H5 is probably the best all round steel to use for general purpose work where everything has to be tackled and the expense of special steel for a particular job cannot easily be justified.

I hope that what has been written will be of use when doing those boring jobs. No longer will the adrenalin be running with excitement as you think to yourself "will it or won't it stay in the chuck" or "if it comes out while working will it hit me in the ear or somewhere more painful?" The work can now be clamped down on the saddle quite secure. Our between centre bar will trundle up and down absolutely free and in fact the whole thing will be plain boring.

# A Simple Indicator

This simple and quickly made device is designed to save time when setting up, although there is no subsitute for a clock gauge when trying to set work true on the faceplate or in the four jaw chuck, or indeed in a milling machine. Personally I find that setting clock gauges up is time-consuming and fiddly and frequently we do not really need the amount of accuracy that they give. Most people in these circumstances use a tool or scriber and judge the accuracy by putting a piece of white paper underneath and seeing how close the appliance is to the work. The little instrument described takes less than an hour to make and will give a reasonable degree of accuracy; it could also suit those who just plainly cannot afford a clock gauge.

It consists of a square steel bar of suitable length and width to fit the tool post. Screwed to this is a steel plate ⅛in. thick and about 1½in. wide. These measurements are not important, being a matter of using a size suitable for your lathe. If you have a Unimat you will probably need a ¼in. square bar for the support with maybe a 1in. wide plate, for a Myford ML7 I used a ½in. bar with 1½in. plate. The plate must however be at least ⅛in. thick. Clamp the two together and drill through, after centre punching, using the tapping size drill for whatever size screws you wish to make use of. Open out and countersink the holes in the plate and screw the pair together. Put some form of marking fluid on the plate. (I used a felt tipped pen). Mount the gadget in the toolpost, put a scriber in the chuck and scribe a line along the plate. Make centre punch marks on that line a quarter of an inch from the front and 2⁵⁄₁₆in. also from the

*The finished indicator.*

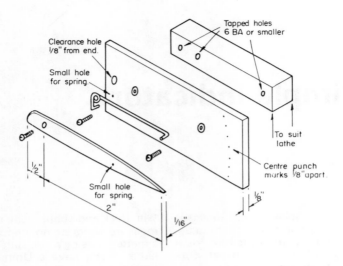

Clearance hole
1/8" from end

Small hole
for spring

Tapped holes
6 BA or smaller

To suit
lathe

Centre punch
marks 1/8" apart.

Small hole
for spring

1/2"

2"

1/16"

1/8"

front. At the same time, with a pair of dividers, scribe an arc using the front centre punch mark as the pivot. The arc is for marking off later on. The hole at a quarter of an inch should be drilled and tapped 6BA, or smaller if making up the tool for a very small lathe. It is there to take the screw on which the arm will pivot.

The arm itself is made from 1/16in. steel strip, and should have a line scribed along the centre and then be centre punched and drilled clearance size for the pivot screw, a half inch from the front end. Two inches along from the same end another centre punch mark is made and a hole drilled in it with about a number 55 drill. This hole is for the spring. The pointer is now filed to shape with a round nose and a sharp point at the rear. The measurements here are more critical. From the centre-line of the pivot hole it should be 1/2in. to the front and 2in. to the back. If

possible, the arm should then be case-hardened by heating up to cherry red, rolling in case-hardening compound, then reheating to cherry red and quenching in a bucket of water. It can be done with an ordinary blowlamp or even on a gas stove. The spring is now wound from 22 s.w.g. piano wire and the ends bent up as shown. It needs only one turn and this can be easily made round the actual pivot screw. After the spring is made, drill a small hole to accept it in the body of the tool, in line with the pivot hole. Then mark off along the previously scribed arc for the centre punch marks at the rear using a pair of dividers. These marks are an eighth of an inch apart and the best way is to set the dividers to 3/8in. Mark off from the centre one mark each side and centre punch each. Set the dividers to 1/2in. and scribe inwards from the marks at 3/8in. and outwards from the centre. Centre punch these

*The component
parts of the
indicator.*

and then set the dividers to ¾in. and scribe off the last two marks from the outside ones. This may sound long-winded but trying to set dividers to ⅛in. and use them is not easy and the way described works out better.

The whole lot can now be cleaned up and assembled. I put a washer each side of the spring to make the arm work easily. It goes without saying that the pivot screw, which is an ordinary bolt, should not be tightened down too much. In use, the amount of variation of the round nose touching the work is multiplied and can be seen in relation to the centre punch marks; with experience quite a degree of accuracy can be obtained by judging the distance between the marks.

# Entertainment & Education for the Practical Model Engineer

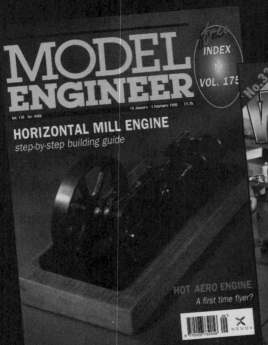

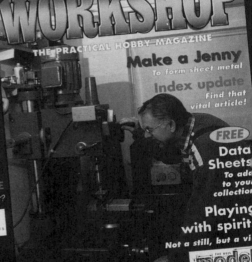

Available from all good newsagents, model and hobby shops.

*Please write for further information:*
**Nexus Special Interests,
Boundary Way,
Hemel Hempstead,
Herts. HP2 7ST**